POLYOMINOES

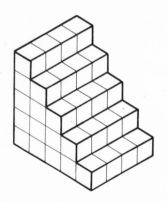

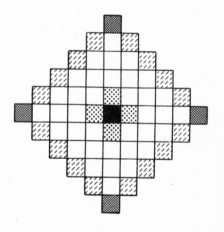

SOLOMON W. GOLOMB

Polyominoes

with more than 190 diagrams

by WARREN LUSHBAUGH

CHARLES SCRIBNER'S SONS, *NEW YORK*

123339

PRINTED IN THE UNITED STATES OF AMERICA

Library of Congress Catalog Card Number 64-24805

For Astrid and Beatrice

Contents

POLYOMINOES

PREFACE

EVER since I "invented" polyominoes in 1953 in a talk to the Harvard Mathematics Club, I have found myself irrevocably committed to their care and feeding. A steady stream of correspondents from around the world and from every stratum of society—board chairmen of leading universities, residents of obscure monasteries, inmates of prominent penitentiaries—have asked for further information, posed new problems, or furnished novel solutions.

With the passage of time, I learned of the true antiquity of pentominoes, one kind of polyomino. Although the name was coined in my lecture of 1953, the first pentomino *problem* was published in 1907 in the *Canterbury Puzzles,* written by the great English inventor of puzzles, Henry Ernest Dudeney; and the observation that there are 12 distinctive patterns (the pentominoes) that can be formed by 5 connected stones on a Go board (the very old Japanese game is played with black and white stone markers placed on a board) is attributed to an ancient master of that game. Moreover, an extensive literature on the subject (under the heading of "dissection problems" rather than "polyominoes") had appeared during the 1930's and 1940's in the *Fairy Chess Review,* a British puzzle journal.

A year after it had been delivered, my Harvard talk was published in *American Mathematical Monthly,* where it attracted the attention of a number of professional mathematicians. However, it was the reprinting of some of this material in the May, 1957, issue of *Scientific American* that brought polyominoes to the attention of a vast reading public.

Since 1957, many groups of high school and college students and teachers have requested lectures on polyominoes, and as well as delivering many talks about this mathematical   13

PREFACE

recreation, I have written numerous articles about it. Polyominoes not only have wide appeal among mathematical-recreations fans, they also serve as fascinating "enrichment" material in school mathematics programs. The lectures, articles, and voluminous correspondence have all helped to precipitate the present book.

Grateful appreciation is expressed to the former publication, *Recreational Mathematics Magazine,* and its Editor, Joseph S. Madachy, for permission to incorporate material that first appeared in that publication. The author is also grateful to *Scientific American* for permission to use material previously published in Martin Gardner's "Mathematical Games" column.

The tolerance of the Jet Propulsion Laboratory and its Director, Dr. W. H. Pickering, of my extracurricular interest in polyominoes during a long association with that organization is deeply appreciated. The meticulous typing and manuscript preparation of Mrs. Julie Jacobs deserves special commendation. Invaluable assistance in editing, proofreading, figure preparation, and problem selection—including the Problem Compendium at the end of this book—was supplied by Mr. Warren Lushbaugh, whose active participation accelerated the completion of the manuscript by many months. Finally, the contributions of a vast army of polyomino fans cannot go unnoticed; special mention must be made of David Klarner and Spencer Earnshaw, who removed many of the most difficult problems from the "unsolved" category.

SOLOMON W. GOLOMB

University of Southern California,
Los Angeles

14

NOTE ON MATERIALS

Most problems in this book consist of finding ways to fit together *polyominoes,* various shapes composed of certain numbers of connected squares. In order to try to form the patterns specified in the puzzles, the reader will need the polyomino pieces, which can easily be made from inexpensive and readily available materials.

All the possible *pentominoes,* polyominoes of 5 squares, are included in a pocket in the back of the book. The unit square from which they have been constructed is $\frac{3}{4}$ inch on a side (though the unit square may be of any convenient size). When the other polyominoes are made, each square of each piece should be the same size as the pentomino unit square provided. Drawings of the polyomino shapes you will use appear on pages 15 and 24.

Heavy cardboard is a good material out of which to cut the polyominoes (paper is not as good because of its lack of durability and tendency to curl at the edges). The shapes of the pieces can be seen in the illustrations, and they can be drawn to the correct scale on the cardboard; the polyominoes can then be cut out with a single-edged razor blade, X-acto knife, or, if the board is thin enough, a sharp scissors. If it is desired to construct additional pentomino sets, they can be made from the heavy cardboard, using the $\frac{3}{4}$ inch unit square and following the shapes on page 19.

In many of the problems, the polyominoes are placed on 8 × 8 checkerboards (8 squares in each horizontal row and 8 squares in each vertical row) and other, smaller areas divided into squares (for example, the 2 × 2 and the 4 × 4 boards). The boards can be made by ruling squares on sheets of cardboard. On all of them, each square should be the same size as the unit square used to make the polyominoes ($\frac{3}{4}$ inch). If, in the case of the domino "masonry" problems, a set of domino tiles used to play the game of dominoes is

15

available, the reader must be careful to make a special board with squares the exact size of one of the domino squares.

The triangular "animals" of some constructions (see pages 128–131) can also be cut out of cardboard, using the $\frac{3}{4}$ inch side of the unit square for all sides of the equilateral triangles. As a preliminary step, isometric graph paper can be used to draw out the triangle guide lines.

Solid polyominoes (see pages 112–115) are constructed from cubes rather than from squares. All the cubes from which the solid pieces are made should be of the same size. One source of materials, though rather expensive, is the small children's alphabet blocks available at toy stores, which can be glued together to form the desired shapes. A less expensive method involves square wooden molding, available at lumber yards, which can be sawed into cubes. The $\frac{3}{4}$ inch stock can be cut into cubes $\frac{3}{4}$ inch on a side; these can then be glued together to form a good size of solid polyominoes.

POLYOMINOES

CHAPTER I

Polyominoes and Checkerboards

THIS book explores polyominoes, shapes made by connecting certain numbers of equal-sized squares, each joined together with at least 1 other square along an edge. (Chess players might call this "rook-wise connection"; that is, a rook—which can travel either horizontally or vertically in any one move, but never diagonally—placed on any square of the polyomino must be able to travel to any other in a finite number of moves.)

Polyomino patterns are actually examples of *combinatorial geometry,* that branch of mathematics dealing with the ways in which geometrical shapes can be combined. It is a frequently neglected aspect of mathematics because it seems to have few general methods, and because in it systematic rules have not replaced ingenuity as the key to discovery. Many of the design problems in practical engineering are combinatorial in nature, especially when standard components or shapes are to be fitted together in some optimal fashion. The aim of this chapter is twofold: first, to serve as an introduction to the mathematical recreation of polyominoes; and second, to illustrate some of the thinking that can be used effectively whenever problems in combinatorial geometry arise.

The simpler polyominoes—all the possible shapes composed of fewer than 5 connected squares—are shown in Figure 1. In the combinatorial problems that follow it will be assumed that polyominoes can be *rotated* (turned 90, 180, or 270 degrees) or *reflected* (flipped over) at will unless otherwise specified (see the section on one-sided polyominoes, page 105).

Figure 1. The simpler polyomino shapes.

Monomino

Domino

Straight Tromino

Right Tromino

Straight Tetromino

Square Tetromino

T Tetromino

Skew Tetromino

L Tetromino

19

POLYOMINOES

Figure 2. Checkerboard with opposite corners deleted.

Figure 3. The 3-colored checkerboard.

Key:

Red

White

Blue

DOMINOES

A *domino* is made of 2 connected squares and has only one shape, a rectangle. The first problem, with which some readers of this book may be familiar, concerns dominoes: Given a checkerboard with a pair of diagonally opposite corner squares deleted (see Figure 2) and a box of dominoes, each of which covers exactly 2 squares, is it possible to cover this board completely with dominoes (allowing no vacant squares and no overlaps)?

The answer is no, and a remarkable proof can be given. The standard checkerboard contains 64 squares of alternating light and dark colors (referred to hereafter as *checkerboard coloring*). On this board, each domino will cover 1 light square and 1 dark square. Thus, *n* dominoes (any specific number of dominoes) will cover *n* light squares and *n* dark squares, that is, a number of each equal to the total number of dominoes. However, the defective checkerboard has more dark squares than light ones, so it cannot be covered. This result is really a theorem in combinatorial geometry.

TROMINOES

It is impossible to cover an 8×8 board entirely with *trominoes,* polyominoes of 3 squares, because 64 is not divisible by 3. Instead, it shall be asked: Can the 8×8 board be covered with 21 trominoes and 1 *monomino* (a single square)?

First, suppose 21 straight trominoes are used; the board is colored "patriotically" (see Figure 3), and it is observed that a straight tromino will cover 1 red square, 1 white square, and 1 blue square, no matter where the piece is placed. Thus, 21 straight trominoes will cover 21 each of the red, white, and blue squares. By actual count, 22 red, 21 white, and 21 blue squares are involved in the 3-colored 8×8 board.

If a monomino is placed in the lower left-hand square, the remaining board will consist of 22 red, 21 white, and 20 blue

POLYOMINOES AND CHECKERBOARDS

squares. Thus, the board cannot be covered with 21 straight trominoes and a monomino in the lower left-hand corner. If some other corner had been covered with the monomino, the board could have been rotated until the monomino was at the lower left, and it would then have been possible to proceed as before. All 4 corners, thus, are *symmetric* to one another. That is, the board can be moved by rotation and by reflection in such a way that any corner can be interchanged with any other one. If a construction is impossible in one situation, it remains impossible in any other situation that is symmetric to the first.

Symmetry arguments are very powerful tools in combinatorial geometry. For example, by this reasoning it can be determined that if a monomino is placed on any blue square, or on any white square, or on any square symmetric to a blue or a white, the rest of the board cannot be covered with straight trominoes.

The only red squares not symmetric to blue or white ones are the 4 shown in Figure 4. It already has been proved that if a monomino is placed anywhere *except* on 1 of these 4 squares, the rest of the board cannot be covered with straight trominoes. The symmetry principle suggests that these 4 remaining ones *might* be exceptional. The construction of Figure 5 shows that they actually are. It is possible to cover the checkerboard with 21 straight trominoes and 1 monomino, provided that the monomino is placed on 1 of the 4 exceptional squares.

When another type of tromino is considered, the result is surprisingly different: No matter where on the checkerboard a monomino is placed, the remaining squares always can be covered with 21 right trominoes.

Consider first a 2 × 2 board. Wherever a monomino is placed, the other 3 squares can be covered by a right tromino (see Figure 6). Next consider a 4 × 4 board. Divide it into quarters, each of which is a 2 × 2 board. Let the monomino be placed in 1 of the quarters, say the upper left. The rest of

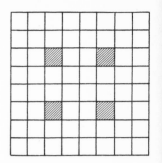

Figure 4. Red squares that are not symmetric to any white or blue squares in the 3-colored checkerboard.

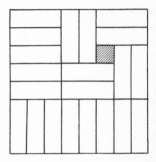

Figure 5. A checkerboard covered by 21 straight trominoes and 1 monomino.

Figure 6. Progressive covering by right trominoes.

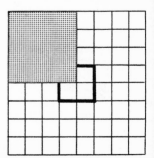

this section can be covered with a right tromino, since it is a 2×2 board. In each of the other 3 quadrants, if a single square is removed, the remaining squares can be covered with a right tromino. And a right tromino placed in the center of the board removes 1 square from each of 3 quadrants, making it possible to complete the covering using only right trominoes.

The 8×8 checkerboard is treated in the same way. First, divide it into quadrants, each of which will be 4×4. The monomino must be in 1 of the 4 sections, each of which can be completed because it is a 4×4 board. The other quadrants can be covered if 1 square is removed from each, for this would make them equivalent to the 4×4 board with the monomino in it. And these 3 extra squares can be juxtaposed to form a right tromino in the center of the board.

The proof just given proceeds by *mathematical induction,* a method of formal mathematical proof. The first board was 2×2; this could also be written as $2^1 \times 2^1$. (The number 2 is called the *base,* and the superscript 1 is the *exponent,* indicating the *power* to which the base should be raised or the number of times it should be multiplied by itself. Thus, 2^1, or 2 to the first power, is simply 2; 2^2 is 2×2, or 4; and 2^3 is $2 \times 2 \times 2$, or 8; 2^n is 2 to the n-th power. The 2×2 board could also be written as $2^n \times 2^n$, when n is equal to 1.) The 2×2 case ($2^n \times 2^n$, $n = 1$) was very easy, and the $2^{n+1} \times 2^{n+1}$ case (for example, $2^{1+1} \times 2^{1+1} = 2^2 \times 2^2 = 4 \times 4$) follows readily from the $2^n \times 2^n$ case. Such proofs are very valuable in combinatorial analysis. They suggest that complex geometrical patterns can be achieved by the systematic repetition and combination of simple patterns.

Figure 7. Any tetrominoes except the skew tetrominoes can be used to cover the checkerboard.

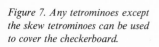

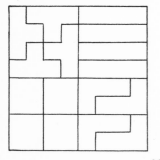

TETROMINOES

Some theorems about *tetrominoes* (polyominoes of 4 squares) are worth mentioning, although detailed proofs will be omitted. Accordingly, each of the following statements may be regarded as a problem exercise.

1. It is easy to cover the checkerboard entirely with straight tetrominoes, square tetrominoes, T tetrominoes, or L tetrominoes. (This is clear from Figure 7.)

2. It is impossible to cover the board, or even a single edge of it, with skew tetrominoes.

3. It is impossible to cover the checkerboard with 15 T tetrominoes and 1 square tetromino. (This can be proved using the ordinary coloring of the board. One must keep track of even, as opposed to odd, numbers of squares covered.)

4. It is likewise impossible to cover the 8 × 8 board with 15 L tetrominoes and 1 square tetromino. (Now, however, the most convenient proof uses the dotted and blank squares of Figure 8.)

5. It is also impossible to cover the board with 1 square tetromino and any combination of straight and skew tetrominoes. (The proof in this case makes use of the wavy-lined and uncolored squares arranged as shown in Figure 9.)

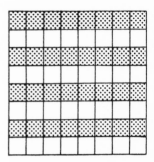

Figure 8. The coloring of the 8 × 8 board used to study coverings by L tetrominoes.

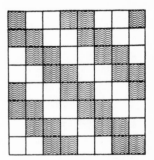

Figure 9. The coloring used to study coverings by straight and skew tetrominoes.

PENTOMINOES

The shapes that cover 5 connected squares are called *pentominoes*. There are 12 of these and the letter "names" in Figure 10 are recommended for them. As a mnemonic device, one has only to remember the end of the alphabet (TUVWXYZ) and the word FILiPiNo. Since there are 12 distinct pentomino shapes, each covering 5 squares, their total area is 60 squares.

Figure 10. The 12 pentominoes.

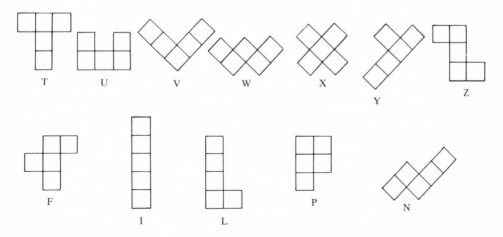

POLYOMINOES

There are numerous ways to place all 12 distinct pentominoes on an 8 × 8 board, with 4 squares always left over. Many interesting patterns can be formed by artistically specifying the positions of the 4 extra squares. Three of these patterns are illustrated in Figure 11.

Figure 11. Three patterns with all 12 distinct pentominoes on a single checkerboard.

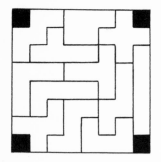
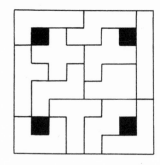
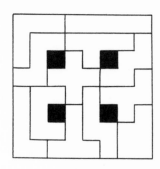

Another obvious possibility is to require that the 4 surplus squares form a 2 × 2 area (a square tetromino) in some specified position on the board. (Two favorite locations are the center and one of the corners.) This placement results in a very remarkable theorem, which can be proved using only 3 constructions: Wherever on the checkerboard a square tetromino is placed, the rest of the board can be covered with the 12 pentominoes.

At first glance, there are 49 possible locations for the square tetromino, and the heavy dots in Figure 12 designate these positions for the center of the 2 × 2 square. However, when symmetry principles are applied, the problem reduces to the 10 nonsymmetric positions indicated by the dots in Figure 13.

A clever stratagem is to combine the square tetromino with the V pentomino to form a 3 × 3 square, as shown in Figure 14.

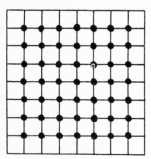

Figure 12. The 49 possible positions for the center of a square tetromino on the checkerboard.

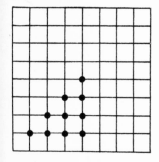

Figure 13. The 10 nonsymmetric positions for a square tetromino on the checkerboard.

Figure 14. The combination of a square tetromino and a V pentomino into a 3 × 3 square.

Then, the 3 diagrams of Figure 15 show the complete proof, because any of the 10 positions for the square tetromino can be realized by first selecting the correct diagram and then utilizing the proper position for the 2×2 square within the 3×3 square.

Figure 15. Three constructions prove that anywhere a 2×2 square is removed from the checkerboard, the remaining 60 squares can be covered by the 12 distinct pentominoes.

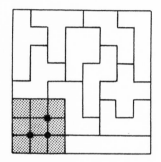
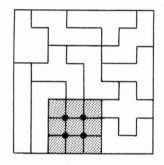
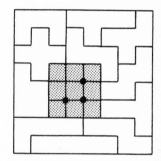

It is also natural to inquire: What is the *least* number of pentominoes that will span the checkerboard? That is, *some of the pentominoes are placed on the board in such a way that none of the remaining ones can be added.* The minimum number needed to span the board is 5, and one such configuration is shown in Figure 16.

Many other patterns can be formed using the 12 pentominoes, and the reader may wish to try some of them. Such configurations include rectangles of 6×10, 5×12, 4×15, and 3×20. The most difficult of these rectangles is the 3×20, and the solution given in Figure 17 is known to be unique, except for the possibility of rotating the shaded central portion by 180 degrees.

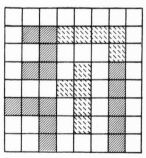

Figure 16. Five pentominoes span the checkerboard.

Figure 17. The 12 pentominoes form a 3×20 rectangle.

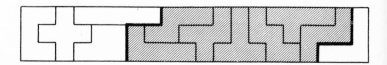

R. M. Robinson, Professor of Mathematics at the University of California at Berkeley, has proposed another fascinating construction with pentominoes, which he calls the "triplication problem": Given a pentomino, use 9 of the other pentominoes to construct a scale model, 3 times as wide and 3 times as high as the given piece. Solutions are shown in Figure 18 for the V and X pentominoes. The reader is invited to try to triplicate the other 10 pentominoes; all of these constructions are known to be possible.

Figure 18. Triplication of the V pentomino and the X pentomino.

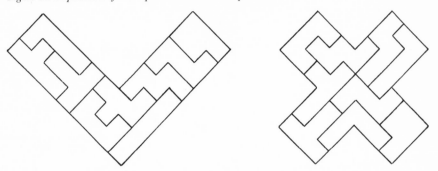

Besides its fascination as a puzzle, the placement of pentominoes on the checkerboard can also make an exciting competitive game. Two or more persons play with one set of the 12 pieces, each player placing a pentomino of his choice on an initially empty checkerboard. The first person who is unable to find room on the board for any of the unused pentominoes is the loser. If all 12 pentominoes are successfully placed on the board, the player who placed the last piece is the winner. The game will last at least 5, and at most 12, moves, can never result in a draw, has more possible openings than chess, and will intrigue players of all ages. It is difficult to advise what strategy should be followed, but there are two valuable strategic principles:

1. Try to move in such a way that there will be room for an *even number* of pieces. (This applies only when there are 2 players.)

2. If a player cannot analyze the situation, he should do something to complicate the placement so that the next player will have even more difficulty analyzing it than he did.

26

The following is a pentomino problem of a rather different nature from those that have been discussed: A man wishes to construct the 12 pentominoes out of plywood. His saw will not cut around corners. What is the smallest plywood rectangle from which he can cut all 12 pentominoes? (The U pentomino, shaded in Figure 19, will require special effort. Assume that it must be cut as a 2 × 3 *hexomino,* a polyomino of 6 squares, and finished later.) The best answer is not known, but a 6 × 13 rectangle may be used. In the illustration (Figure 19), the heavier lines are to be cut first, starting from the sides and working inward.

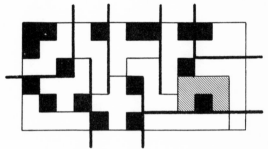

Figure 19. The 12 pentominoes to be cut from a 6 × 13 rectangle.

There is a lesson in plausible reasoning to be learned from the pentominoes. Given certain basic data, one labors long and hard to fit them into a pattern. Having succeeded, one then believes the pattern to be the *only* one that "fits the facts," indeed, that the data are merely manifestations of the beautiful, comprehensive whole constructed from them. The pentominoes illustrate that many different patterns may be constructed from the same data, all equally valid, and that the nature of the final pattern is determined more by the desired shape than by the information at hand. It is also possible that, for certain data, no pattern of the type the constructor is conditioned to seek may exist. This will be illustrated by the hexominoes.

HEXOMINOES

There are 35 distinct hexominoes and 108 distinct *heptominoes* (polyominoes of 7 squares). No one has yet succeeded in obtaining an expression or formula for the exact number   27

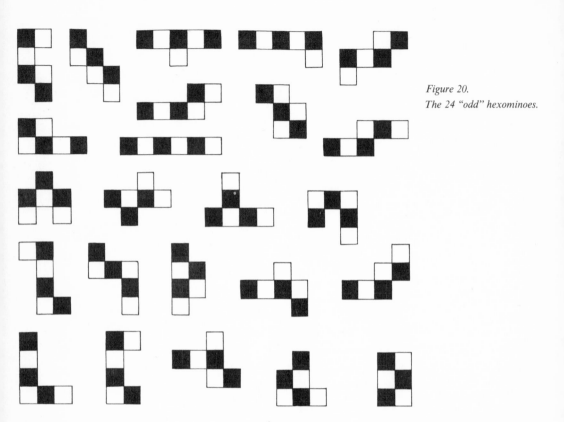

Figure 20.
The 24 "odd" hexominoes.

of *n*-ominoes as a function of *n*; that is, a formula that will give the number of differently shaped polyominoes for any specified number of connected squares. Combinatorial problems of this sort are often tantalizingly difficult. Partial results of calculations on this "polyomino enumeration problem" will be taken up in Chapter VI.

The 35 hexominoes cover a total area of 210 squares. It is natural to try to arrange them in rectangles, either 3×70, 5×42, 6×35, 7×30, 10×21, or 14×15. All such attempts, however, will fail. To prove this, in each of the rectangles checkerboard coloring could be introduced, resulting in 105 light and 105 dark squares, an *odd* number of

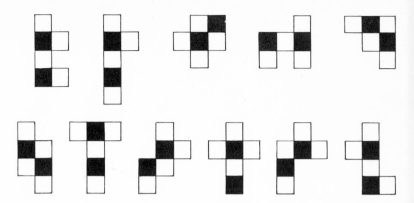

Figure 20 continued.

The 11 "even" hexominoes.

each. There are 24 hexominoes that always will cover 3 dark squares and 3 light squares (an odd number of each). But the other 11 hexominoes always cover 2 squares of one color and 4 of the other, an *even* number of each. The 35 hexominoes are shown in Figure 20 according to their checkerboard-covering characteristics.

There are an even number of "odd" hexominoes and an odd number of "even" hexominoes. Since in all multiplication "even times odd equals even" and "odd times even equals even," the 35 hexominoes always will cover an even number of light squares and an even number of dark squares. However, the number of light (or dark) squares is 105 for any of the rectangles in question, and 105 is odd, so the construction is impossible.

It is noteworthy that the same checkerboard coloring—that is, the alternation of light and dark squares—used to prove the simplest fact about dominoes also serves to prove a far more complex theorem about hexominoes. The underlying theme of this coloring is *parity check,* or a check for evenness, a simple, yet powerful, mathematical tool based on the obvious fact that an even number is never equal to an odd number. The use of "colors" is a valuable aid to the intuition—objects colored differently will seldom be confused. And sometimes, as in the straight-tromino problem, the colors vividly proclaim a solution that might otherwise have been overlooked.

CHAPTER II

Patterns and Polyominoes

CHAPTER I introduced polyominoes and presented problems that use these shapes in attempts to cover squares and rectangles of various sizes. The present chapter is devoted to a variety of problems that involve fitting these polyominoes together into other specified shapes and patterns.

PENTOMINO PATTERNS

A new class of pentomino patterns to be discussed here are the *superposition* problems, the construction of 2 or more shapes all of whose parts coincide. Several examples will now be considered.

1. The reader is challenged to arrange the 12 pentominoes into *two* 5 × 6 rectangles of 6 pentominoes each; the 2 sets are drawn in Figure 21. The choice of sets shown is unique. In the solution of the rectangle made from the set on the right, the F and N pentominoes can be fitted together in another distinct way and still occupy the same region. Note that the answer to this superposition problem simultaneously solves the 5 × 12 and the 6 × 10 rectangle problems simply by putting the two 5 × 6 rectangles together in 2 different ways.

2. Find solutions to the 8 × 8 pattern with the 4-square hole in the middle so that the pieces will separate into 2 congruent parts, each using 6 of the pentominoes. Three typical arrangements are shown in Figure 22.

3. Divide the 12 pentominoes into 3 groups of 4 each. Find one 20-square region that *each* of the 3 groups will cover. One solution is shown in Figure 23, but several other answers to this problem have been discovered, and the reader is invited to look for his own.

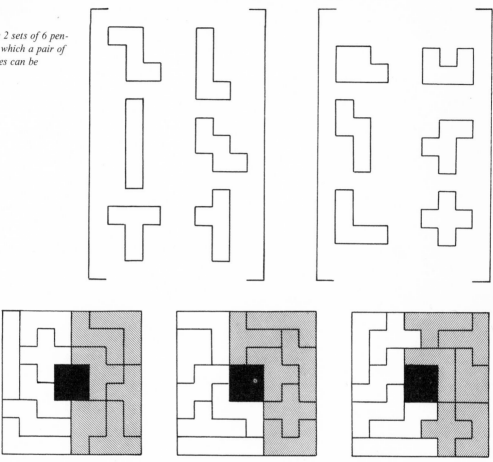

Figure 21. The 2 sets of 6 pentominoes from which a pair of
× 6 rectangles can be
constructed.

Figure 22. Typical solutions to the 8 × 8 board with a 2 × 2 hole and 2 congruent pieces.

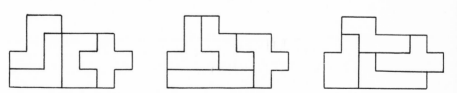

Figure 23. A solution to the "3 congruent groups" problem.

31

4. Divide the 12 pentominoes again into 3 groups of 4 each. Subdivide each group into 2 pairs of pentominoes. For each group, find a 10-square region that both of its pairs will cover. One solution is given in Figure 24. It is interesting to find other configurations, especially those eliminating "holes" in all 3 regions. The reader may wish to look for a different solution with holes and for one without holes; these do exist.

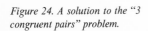

Figure 24. A solution to the "3 congruent pairs" problem.

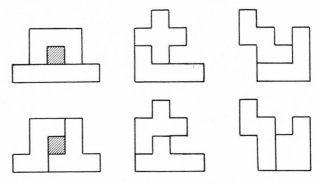

Figure 25. Solution to the three 3 × 7 rectangles of pentominoes.

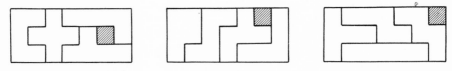

5. Once more, divide the 12 pentominoes into 3 groups of 4 each. To each group add a monomino and form a 3 × 7 rectangle (see Figure 25). This solution is known to be unique, except that in the first rectangle the monomino and the Y pentomino can be rearranged and still occupy the same region.

32

The uniqueness proof follows a suggestion of Dr. C. S. Lorens, an engineer employed by the Aerospace Corporation in Los Angeles. To begin with, the X pentomino can be used only in conjunction with the U pentomino in the pattern shown in Figure 26. Next, neither the F nor the W pentomino can be used to complete this rectangle. Also, with the U pentomino needed to support the X, it is impossible to use both the F and W in the same 3 × 7 rectangle. Hence, of the three 3 × 7 rectangles, one will contain X, U, another will contain W (but not U), and the third will contain F (but not U). When all possible completions of these 3 rectangles are listed and compared (a very time-consuming enterprise), it is found that the only possible solution is given in Figure 25.

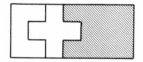

Figure 26. The only location for the X pentomino in a 3 × 7 rectangle.

6. Divide the 12 pentominoes into 4 groups of 3 each. Find a 15-square region that *each* of the 4 groups will cover exactly. No solution to this problem is known. On the other hand, the configuration has not been proved impossible.

7. Find the smallest region on the checkerboard onto which each of the 12 pentominoes will fit, one at a time. The minimum area is 9 squares, and the 2 regions are shown in Figure 27.

Figure 27. Minimal regions on which each of the 12 pentominoes can fit.

The adequacy of these minimal areas is proved by observing that each pentomino, when placed in the area, does fit.   33

The impossibility of the adequacy of *fewer* than 9 squares is shown as follows. If it were possible to use an area of fewer than 9 squares, then the I, X, and V pentominoes would fit on a region of no more than 8 squares. The I and X pentominoes would then have 3 squares in common. (Otherwise, either 9 squares are needed for the I and X, or else the center square of the X coincides with an end square of the I, and 9 squares would be required as soon as the V pentomino is considered.) This can be constructed in 2 distinct ways, as shown in Figure 28. In either case, the position of the V pentomino is then specified. However, the placing of the U pentomino would then require 1 more square. Thus, 8 squares are not enough, whereas 9 have been shown by example to be sufficient.

Figure 28. Minimum regions for the I, X, and V pentominoes.

Several years ago, the resources of modern electronic computing were devoted to various pentomino problems. A technical report (for bibliographic information on all material cited in the text, see the Bibliography) by the American logician Dana S. Scott, Professor of Philosophy at Stanford University in California, describes 2 constructions that were solved by the MANIAC computer. The first problem was how to fit the 12 pentominoes onto a 3×20 rectangle. It was verified that the 2 solutions already known are indeed the only possible ones. The second problem was to find all the ways to fit the 12 pentominoes onto the 8×8 board, leaving a 2×2 hole in the center. It was discovered that there are 65 basically different solutions (in the sense that 2 solutions differing only by rotation or reflection of the board are not regarded as distinct). The program included the astute observation that there are only 3 basically different locations for the X pentomino, as shown in Figure 29. It is

34

Figure 29. The 3 possible locations for the X pentomino on the 8 × 8 board with a 2 × 2 center hole.

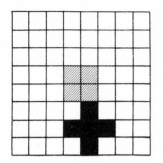 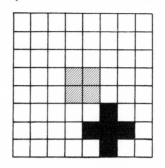 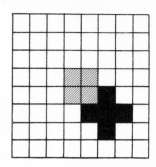

possible to finish covering the board in each of these cases in 20, 19, and 26 different ways, respectively. Three of the more interesting solutions are shown in Figure 30. A number of otherwise plausible situations turn out to be impossible, since they are absent from Scott's listing. These include the configurations shown in Figure 31.

Figure 30. Three interesting solutions to the 8 × 8 board with a 2 × 2 center hole.

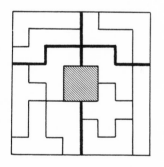 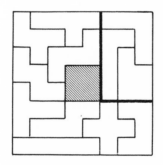 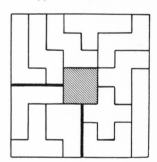

Figure 31. Impossible pentomino constructions for the 8 × 8 board.

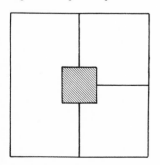 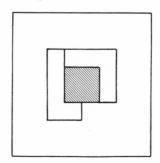 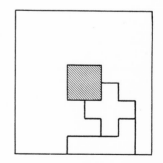

Professor C. B. Haselgrove of Manchester University in England, an astronomer known for his contributions to number theory, recently programmed a computer to find all the ways of arranging the 12 pentominoes into a 6 × 10 rectangle. Excluding rotations and reflections, he found 2,339 basically distinct solutions! He also verified the results of Dana Scott's 2 programs.

Before leaving the subject of pentomino patterns, several special configuration problems seem worthy of mention:

1. The 64-square triangle, filled with the 12 pentominoes and the square tetromino. (Other tetrominoes may also be specified as the thirteenth piece.) One solution is shown in Figure 32.

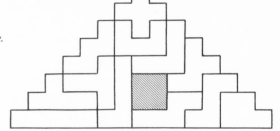

Figure 32. The 64-square triangle.

2. Another difficult configuration is the elongated cross of Figure 33.

Figure 33. An elongated cross composed of pentominoes.

3. It was easily proved by Professor R. M. Robinson (who also first proposed the jagged square of Chapter VI) that the 60-square pattern shown in Figure 34 is incapable of holding the 12 pentominoes.

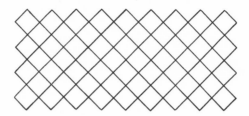

Figure 34. R. M. Robinson's 60-square region.

In particular, there are 22 edge squares (including corners) in this pattern. If the pentominoes are examined separately, and the maximum number of edge squares each could contribute is listed, the total is only 21, as follows:

T = 1	W = 3	Z = 1	L = 1	
U = 1	X = 3	F = 3	P = 2	Total = 21
V = 1	Y = 2	I = 1	N = 2	

This type of reasoning is used in solving jigsaw puzzles, where it is common practice to separate the edge pieces from the interior ones.

Two other interesting pentomino patterns are dealt with in Chapter IV.

TETROMINO PROBLEMS

Unlike the pentominoes, the 5 distinct tetrominoes will not form a rectangle. To prove this, color rectangles 20 squares in area in checkerboard fashion, as indicated in Figure 35. Four of the 5 tetrominoes will always cover an equal

Figure 35. Checkerboard colorings of the 2 × 10 and 4 × 5 rectangles.

number of dark and light squares. However, the remaining tetromino always covers 3 squares of one color and 1 square of the other (see Figure 36). Hence, the 5 tetrominoes will cover a total of an *odd* number of dark squares and an *odd* number of light squares. However, the rectangles in Figure 35 have 10 squares of each color, and 10 is an even number.

Figure 36. The 4 "balanced" tetrominoes and, at the far right, the "unbalanced" tetromino.

On the other hand, any of several different pentominoes can be combined with the 5 tetrominoes to form a 5 × 5 square. Two examples are given in Figure 37. The reader is invited to investigate how many *different* pentominoes can be used in this manner.

Figure 37. The tetrominoes may combine with a pentomino to form a 5 × 5 square.

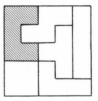 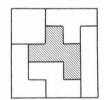

MASONRY PROBLEMS

Robert I. Jewett, while a graduate student in mathematics at the University of Oregon, proposed the following problem: Is it possible to cover a rectangle with 2 or more dominoes so that every *grid line* (that is, the lines, both horizontal and vertical, spaced at the width of 1 domino and extending perpendicularly between parallel edges) of the rectangle intersects at least 1 domino? For example, in the pattern of Figure 38, the vertical grid line in the middle of the rectangle does not cut any dominoes. Thinking of dominoes as bricks, such a grid line represents a structural weakness. Jewett's problem is thus to find "masonry" patterns without "fault lines."

Figure 38. A rectangle of dominoes, with a fault line.

Many people who try this problem soon give up, convinced that there are no solutions. Actually, there are infinitely many, but the one using the smallest number of dominoes requires 15 of them, arranged in a 5 × 6 rectangle. In fact, there are 2 basically different ways to form such a rectangle, as shown in Figure 39.

Figure 39. Two fault-free 5 × 6 rectangles of dominoes.

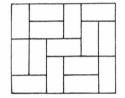
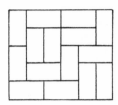

It is not difficult to show that the minimum width for fault-free rectangles must exceed 4 squares. (The case of width 2 [a rectangle 2 squares wide] is easily ruled out as soon as covering one of the width-2 sides of the rectangle is attempted. Either 1 domino covers both squares forming the side, producing a fault line immediately, or else 2 separate dominoes cover the 2 squares, also producing a fault line. The reader is invited to rule out the cases of width 3 and width 4.) Hence, since 5 × 5 is an odd number of squares, while dominoes always cover an even number, the 5 × 6 rectangle is the smallest possible construction.

A 5 × 6 rectangle can be "extended" to the 8 × 8 checkerboard and still satisfy the fault-free condition. In particular, this can be done as indicated in Figure 40. Surprisingly, there are no fault-free 6 × 6 squares. There is a remarkable proof for this: Imagine any 6 × 6 square covered entirely with dominoes. Such a figure contains 18 dominoes (half the total number of squares) and 10 grid lines (5 horizontal and 5 vertical). One such covering (*not* fault free) is shown in Figure 41. The grid lines that have not been intersected are indicated by heavy lines.

As noted earlier, such a figure is fault free only if each grid line intersects at least 1 domino. (Note that each domino is cut by *exactly* 1 grid line.) It will be shown that each grid

Figure 40. Extending a fault-free 5 × 6 rectangle to a fault-free 8 × 8 rectangle.

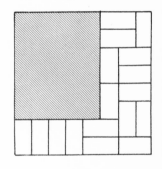

Figure 41. A 6 × 6 rectangle covered with dominoes (not fault free).

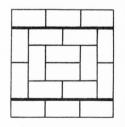

39

line intersects an *even number* of dominoes. Hence, in the fault-free case, each grid line must intersect at least 2 dominoes. With 10 grid lines, at least 20 dominoes would be intersected; but there are only 18 of them on the 6 × 6 board.

It remains only to prove the assertion that each grid cuts an even number of dominoes. Consider, for example, a vertical grid line. The area to the left of it is an *even* number of squares (6, 12, 18, and so on). The dominoes entirely to the left (that is, not intersected by the grid line) cover an even number of squares, since each domino covers 2. The dominoes cut by the grid line must also occupy an even area to the left of it, because this area is the difference between 2 even numbers (the total area to the left and the area of the uncut dominoes to the left). Since each cut domino occupies 1 square to the left of the grid line, there must be an *even number* of dominoes cut by the grid line. Thus the proof is complete.

Similar reasoning shows that for a fault-free 6 × 8 rectangle to exist, every grid line must intersect *exactly* 2 dominoes. This is precisely what happens in the example shown in Figure 42.

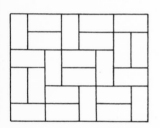

Figure 42. A fault-free 6 × 8 rectangle, where every grid line cuts exactly 2 dominoes.

The most general result is the following: If a rectangle has an area that is an even number of units, and if both its length and width exceed 4, it is possible to find a fault-free domino covering of the rectangle, except in the 6 × 6 case. Actually, coverings for all larger rectangles can be extended from the 5 × 6 and the 6 × 8 rectangles, using a method of enlarging either the length or the width by 2. This procedure is easiest to explain by example. In Figure 43 the extension of a 5 × 6 rectangle to a 5 × 8 rectangle is shown. Gen-

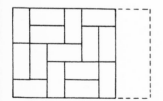

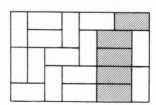

Figure 43. Extending the length (or width) of a fault-free rectangle by 2.

erally, to extend a rectangle horizontally by 2, a horizontal domino is placed next to each horizontal one at the old boundary, while vertical dominoes are shifted from the old boundary to the new, leaving an intervening space, which is filled with 2 horizontal dominoes for each vertical domino shifted.

As a concluding problem in masonry patterns, the reader may find it interesting to study *trominoes* as bricks. In particular, what is the smallest rectangle that can be covered by 2 or more straight trominoes without any fault lines?

CHAPTER III

Where Pentominoes Will Not Fit

PENTOMINO EXCLUSION BY MONOMINOES

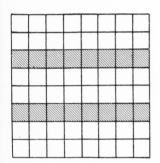

T, U, V, Z excluded

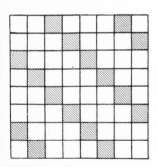

U, Y, I, L excluded

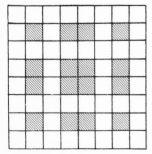

W, F, P, N excluded

THE fitting of pentominoes and other polyominoes into patterns of various shapes has been the theme of the problems thus far. This section's problems will have an opposite objective: namely, what must be done to keep a pentomino *off* the checkerboard? Specifically, for each of the 12 pentominoes, what is the least number of monominoes that can be placed on the 8 × 8 board so that a given pentomino can no longer be fitted onto the board? There are thus 12 distinct problems, 1 for each of the pentominoes. To solve these, it is necessary first to exhibit a way of placing a certain number of monominoes on the checkerboard so as to exclude the given pentomino and then to *prove* (by whatever combinatorial reasoning or tricks suggest themselves) that no fewer monominoes could have been used for the same purpose.

To begin with, it takes only 3 constructions to show that 16 monominoes will always be *sufficient* to exclude any prescribed pentomino. (It will be seen later that, in 6 of the 12 cases, 16 monominoes are also *necessary*.) These 3 placements are shown in Figure 44. Under each board are the names of 4 pentominoes; none of these pieces can be fitted onto that particular partially occupied checkerboard. All 12 pentominoes are thus excludable by 16 monominoes. In fact, 3 of the pentominoes (T, W, and F) are excluded by 2 out of the 3 partially covered boards above.

For some of the pentominoes (notably the U, W, Y, and L), many people experience difficulty in finding as few as 16 locations for monominoes to exclude the given pentomino. However, once the patterns in Figure 44 are found, the im-

Figure 44. Three patterns proving that 16 monominoes are sufficient to exclude any given pentomino from the checkerboard.

provements of Figure 45 are usually discovered quickly. Figure 45*a* exhibits a configuration of only 12 monominoes that succeeds in keeping the X pentomino off the board. Similarly, Figure 45*b* uses only 14 monominoes to keep off the I pentomino. However, much to the dismay of those who have pondered long and hard to find a way to do as well as this, neither of these results is the best possible. To keep the suspense to a minimum, the best configurations for the 12 pentominoes are shown in the 9 constructions of Figure 46.

Simple inspection will verify that the indicated numbers of monominoes, ranging from 10 to 16, are indeed sufficient to exclude the specified pentominoes from the checkerboard. It remains to show that the number of monominoes appearing in Figure 46 are also *necessary*. All 12 necessity proofs are elaborations of the same basic combinatorial theme and will be discussed here in the order of increasing complexity. (The 4 most difficult proofs will be left somewhat incomplete.)

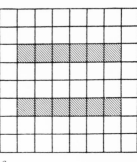

a

b

Fig 45. (a) *Twelve monominoes used to exclude the X.* (b) *Fourteen monominoes used to exclude the I.*

Figure 46. Sufficient numbers of monominoes to exclude indicated pentominoes from the checkerboard.

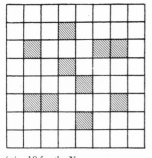

(a)   10 for the X

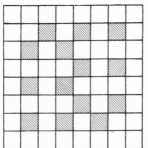

(b)   12 for the I

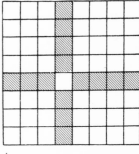

(c)   14 for the T

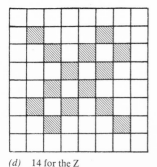

(d)   14 for the Z

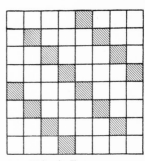

(e)   14 for the F

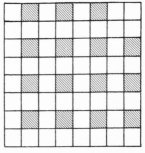

(f)   15 for the W

Figure 46
continued.

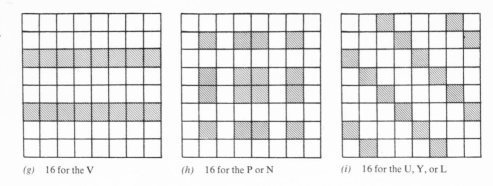

(g) 16 for the V   *(h)* 16 for the P or N   *(i)* 16 for the U, Y, or L

Figure 47. Construction used to show that at least 12 monominoes are necessary to exclude the I pentomino.

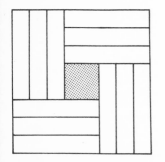

Figure 48. Construction used in the proof that at least 16 monominoes are needed to exclude the Y pentomino.

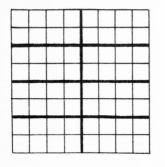

The simplest necessity proof is for the I pentomino. To show that 12 monominoes are necessary to keep the I pentomino off the 8 × 8 board consider the board decomposed as in Figure 47, where there are 12 nonoverlapping 1 × 5 rectangles, each of which could independently hold an I pentomino. To exclude this piece there must be at least 1 monomino in each of the twelve 1 × 5 rectangles. Thus, a minimum of 12 monominoes is necessary to exclude the I pentomino. And, from Figure 46*b*, 12 monominoes is also seen to be sufficient.

Actually, with the sole exception of the I pentomino, it is not possible to fit as many of a given pentomino onto the checkerboard as there are monominoes needed to keep that piece off the board. However, the proof just given is easily modified to treat the 6 pentominoes that actually require 16 monominoes to keep them off the board.

Consider first the Y pentomino and decompose the checkerboard as in Figure 48. To keep the Y pentomino off the board, it is certainly necessary to keep it out of each of the eight 2 × 4 rectangular regions. Moreover, a single monomino will *not* exclude the Y pentomino, there being only 2 inequivalent locations for the monomino: namely, a corner square or an interior square (Figure 49). Neither location will keep the rectangle free of Y pentominoes. Hence, at least 2 monominoes are needed in each of the 8 rectangular regions, making a total of 16 monominoes necessary. Figure 46*i* showed this number to be sufficient as well.

The same decomposition of the board (Figure 48) works for the U, L, P, and N pentominoes also, since none of them is kept off a 2 × 4 rectangle by a single monomino (specifically, see Figure 50).

Figure 49. One monomino is insufficient to exclude the Y from a 2 × 4 rectangle.

Figure 50. One monomino is insufficient to exclude the U, L, P, or N from a 2 × 4 rectangle.

Among the pentominoes requiring 16 monominoes to exclude them, there remains only the V. For this case, decompose the checkerboard into quadrants (Figure 51). To show that each quadrant must contain at least 4 monominoes, suppose there were a quadrant with only 3 monominoes. Then in that section, at least 1 *rank* (horizontal row) and at least 1 *file* (vertical row) must be vacant. A rank of 4 squares intersecting a file of 4 in length will always be able to hold a V pentomino, as shown in Figure 51, where the 3 inequivalent cases (outside rank with outside file, inside rank with inside file, and inside rank with outside file) are illustrated. Hence, each of the 4 quadrants must contain at least 4 monominoes in order to exclude the V, making a total of a minimum of 16 on the entire board.

Figure 51. At least 16 monominoes are needed to exclude the V.

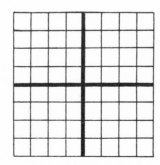

Figure 52. Constructions used in the proof that at least 14 monominoes are needed to exclude the T.

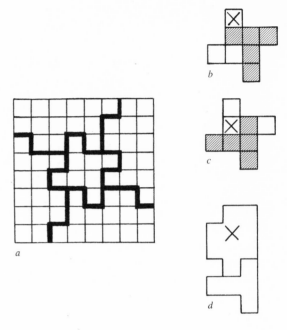

b

c

d

a

The next most simple case is that of the T pentomino. This time, decompose the 8 × 8 board as in Figure 52*a*. There are 5 areas, an 8-square region in the center, and 4 congruent 14-square regions around the edge. The central region cannot exclude the T pentomino with but a single monomino, as a glance at the 2 inequivalent locations for the monomino (Figures 52*b* and 52*c*) indicates. Hence, the central region must contain at least 2 monominoes. To show that each outside region must contain at least 3 monominoes, for a total of at least 4 × 3 + 2 = 14 monominoes on the entire board, suppose the outside area could exclude the T pentomino with only 2 monominoes. Decomposing it as in Figure 52*d*, the region covered by the T pentomino would have to contain a monomino, and there would be only 1 monomino left for the other subregion. The square indicated by a cross is the only monomino location that keeps T pentominoes out

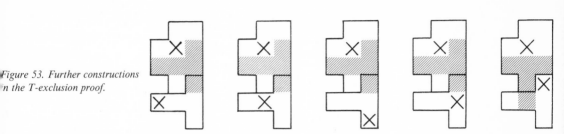

Figure 53. Further constructions in the T-exclusion proof.

of the 9-square subregion. However, as Figure 53 shows, each of the 5 assignments of a monomino to the T portion leaves a loophole somewhere in the 14-square region. Thus, 3 monominoes in each of these regions are necessary, and the 14 monominoes that are shown to be sufficient in Figure 46c are also seen to be necessary.

The remaining 4 pentominoes are more difficult to treat. Of these, the W will be considered first and the 8 × 8 board decomposed as shown in Figure 54. It is rather easy to demonstrate that each of the 5 major subregions requires at least the number of monominoes listed on it to exclude the W pentomino. However, this merely leads to the conclusion that 13 monominoes are necessary, while the objective is to show that, in fact, 15 are necessary.

Suppose 13 monominoes were sufficient. Then, no matter how Figure 54 is rotated, the indicated number of monominoes must exclude the W. Superposition of all the constraints of rotation and reflection leads to Figure 55. Each of the 4 "corner" regions would require 3 monominoes, and the dark region in the center, being congruent to 1 of the corner regions of Figure 54, requires 3 more, for a total of 15. Since this argument began with the assumption that 13 would be adequate, a contradiction has been reached, and 13 has been shown to be insufficient. A lengthy refinement of this argument would show that 15 are necessary. From Figure 46f, this number is also known to be sufficient.

The remaining 3 pentominoes (X, F, and Z) are analogous to the W in their treatment. First, a single illustration can be

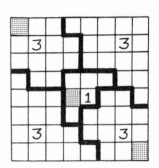

Figure 54. Decomposition used in the W-pentomino exclusion proof.

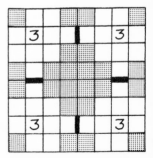

Figure 55. Superposition of constraints imposed by rotations and reflections of Figure 54.

47

*Figure 56. Decomposition showing
monominoes needed to exclude
(a) the X, (b) the F, (c) the Z.*

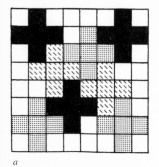

a

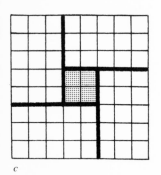

b

c

used to arrive within 2 of the actual number of sufficient monominoes. For example, see Figure 56.

It is seen in 56*a* that at least 8 monominoes are needed to exclude the X; in 56*b*, that at least 12 are needed to exclude the F; and in 56*c*, that at least 12 are needed to exclude the Z.

To show that at least 9 monominoes are needed against the X, consider Figure 57*a*. If 8 monominoes were sufficient, they would have to lie in the 8 X regions of 57*a* no matter how that pattern were rotated and reflected on the checkerboard. That is, all 8 would have to be in the *unshaded* portion of Figure 57*b*. However, the large central region of 57*b* actually requires at least 2 more monominoes to keep out the X, contradicting the sufficiency of the 8 monominoes. Again, further refinement of this argument will show that 10 are necessary.

*Figure 57. Constructions used to
prove that 8 monominoes are
insufficient to exclude the X.*

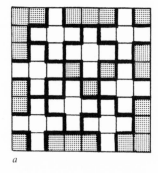

a

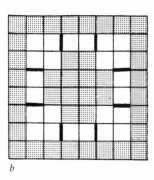

b

For the F, consider Figure 58*a*. The regions require the indicated number of monominoes to exclude the F. To show this for the area with the number 3, consider its decomposition in Figure 58*b*. If 2 monominoes were sufficient, 1 would have to be in the F subregion. The only location for a monomino that would keep an F out of the other subregion is at the square indicated by an *x*. However, any square in the F subregion combined with the *x* square fails to exclude the further occurrence of F's.

48

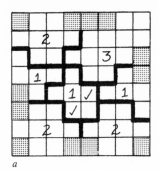

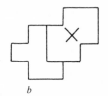

Figure 58. Constructions used to prove that 12 monominoes are insufficient to exclude the F.

a

b

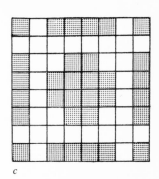

c

The region in 58a with the 2 check marks could hold an F with either checked square excluded. When all the rotations and reflections of 58a are considered, the conclusion is reached that if 12 monominoes would suffice to exclude F's, they would all have to be in the unshaded portion of Figure 58c. However, at least 2 more monominoes would then be needed in the central, shaded region, proving that 12 monominoes are insufficient. Further refinement of this argument leads to the conclusion that 14 monominoes are both necessary and sufficient.

There remains only the case of the Z pentomino. In Figure 59a each of the 4 "corners" is readily shown to require at least 3 monominoes; this is accomplished by the usual expedient: a Z is drawn in the region and it is observed that 1 monomino within the Z and another outside it is insufficient to exclude Z pentominoes.

By rotating and reflecting Figure 59a in all possible ways, it is seen that if 12 monominoes were sufficient to exclude the Z pentomino, then all 12 would lie in the unshaded portion of Figure 59b. However, the shaded portion of 59b actually can contain 4 more Z pentominoes simultaneously. Hence, at least 13 monominoes are needed.

The argument that makes it possible to arrive at 14 as the necessary and sufficient number of monominoes to exclude the Z pentomino will now be sketched. First, divide the checkerboard into the 4 congruent quarters shown in Figure 59c. Suppose that 13 monominoes were sufficient to exclude

Figure 59. Constructions used to prove that 12 monominoes are insufficient to exclude the Z.

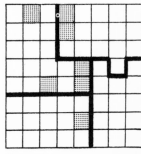

a

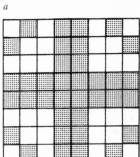

b

c

the Z pentomino (that number already known to be necessary). Then, in the hypothetical 13-monomino configuration, at least 1 of the 4 quarters will contain a minimum of 4 monominoes (since 4 whole numbers, all less than 4, cannot add up to 13).

Rotate the hypothetical 13-monomino configuration so that the upper left-hand quarter has at least 4 monominoes, leaving 9 at most for the rest, and divide the remaining area into the 2 regions shown in Figure 60. Since the smaller, shaded region must contain at least 3 monominoes in order to exclude the Z, 6 at most are available for the large, unshaded region. Proving that 6 monominoes are insufficient to exclude the Z from this large region will thus complete the proof. This will be accomplished by showing that the assumption that 6 monominoes suffice leads to a contradiction.

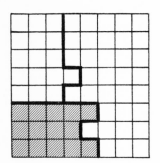

Figure 60. Construction used to contradict the assumption that 13 monominoes suffice to exclude the Z.

If 6 monominoes were enough, they would lie within the 2 unshaded regions of Figure 61a, since each of those regions requires 3 monominoes. They would also lie within the 2 unshaded regions of Figure 61b, as well as the 2 unshaded regions of Figure 61c, d, and e. Combining these results, 6 monominoes, 3 in each of the 2 unshaded regions shown in Figure 61f, must keep the Z pentomino off the entire 34-square region.

Consider the upper portion. Three monominoes in the unshaded portion of Figure 62a must keep the Z pentomino out of the entire 21-square area. It is not difficult to show that 62b illustrates the only way to do this.

The lower portion of Figure 61f is shown in 62c, with 2 additional shaded squares borrowed from 62b. Three monominoes in the unshaded portion must be able to exclude the Z. However, the 2 unshaded squares with dots *must* contain monominoes, since they complete Z's all of whose other squares are shaded. One more monomino cannot now be placed anywhere to exclude the Z pentomino. The proof by contradiction is thus completed; 13 monominoes are insufficient to keep the Z pentomino off the checker-

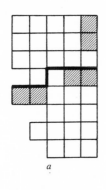
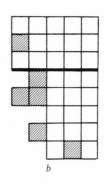
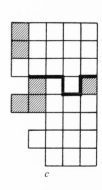

Figure 61. Further constructions used in the Z-pentomino exclusion.

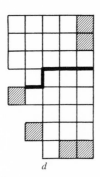
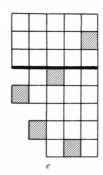
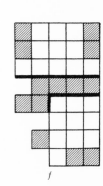

a   b   c

d   e   f

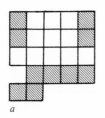
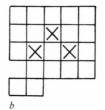
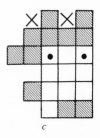

Figure 62. Final constructions in the Z exclusion.

a   b

c

board; 14 monominoes are therefore necessary and, as seen earlier (Figure 46*d*), also sufficient.

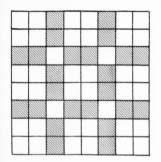

Figure 63. Twelve dominoes must be used to exclude all 12 pentominoes simultaneously.

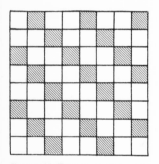

Figure 64. Twenty-one monominoes exclude all but the W pentomino.

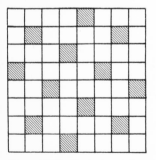

Figure 65. Twelve is the minimum number of monominoes needed to exclude 2 pentominoes (the X and the I).

MODIFICATIONS AND GENERALIZATIONS

A number of interesting variants of the problems in the preceding section can be considered. For example, one can try to find the minimum number of dominoes to be placed on the 8 × 8 checkerboard so as to exclude all 12 pentominoes *simultaneously*. The solution to this problem is shown in Figure 63. If each of these 12 dominoes is regarded as 2 monominoes, it is evident that 24 monominoes suffice to exclude all 12 pentominoes; and no solution with fewer than 24 monominoes is believed to exist.

If one asks for the minimum configuration of monominoes excluding at least 11 of the 12 pentomino shapes, the answer is believed to be as shown in Figure 64. Here, 21 monominoes suffice to exclude all pentominoes except the W.

Another multiple-pentomino exclusion problem is to find the configuration using the fewest monominoes possible to exclude at least 2 of the pentominoes. Since a glance at Figure 46 will reveal that fewer than 12 monominoes can hope to exclude only the X pentomino, it is remarkable that 12 monominoes *can* be placed, as in Figure 65, to exclude both the X and I pentominoes, thereby solving the problem. Altogether, there are 4,095 problems involving the use of monominoes to exclude individual pentominoes, pairs of pentominoes, triples, and on up to exclusion of all 12 pentominoes at once; this leaves many additional exercises for the ambitious reader.

It is also instructive to see how many monominoes are needed to exclude the various polyominoes of lower order than the pentominoes from the checkerboard. The minimal configurations are shown in Figure 66, but the proofs that they are indeed minimal will be left to the reader.

Notice how these patterns already foreshadow most of those in Figure 46. Naturally, a monomino configuration excluding a given polyomino will certainly exclude any ex-

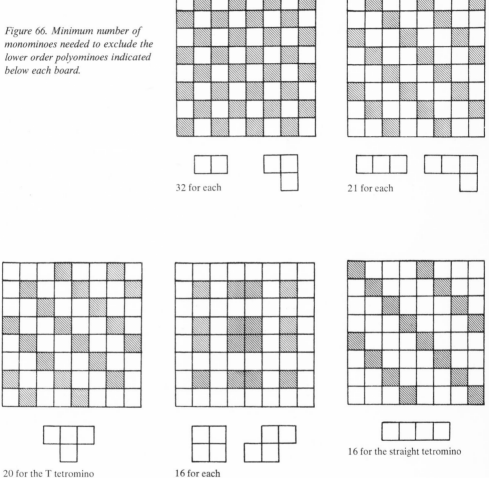

Figure 66. Minimum number of monominoes needed to exclude the lower order polyominoes indicated below each board.

32 for each 21 for each

20 for the T tetromino 16 for each

16 for the straight tetromino

tension of that polyomino, and every pentomino is the extension of at least one, and often several, tetrominoes.

A further insight into the problem of excluding pentominoes from the 8 × 8 board is obtained by studying the related problem of using monominoes to exclude the various

53

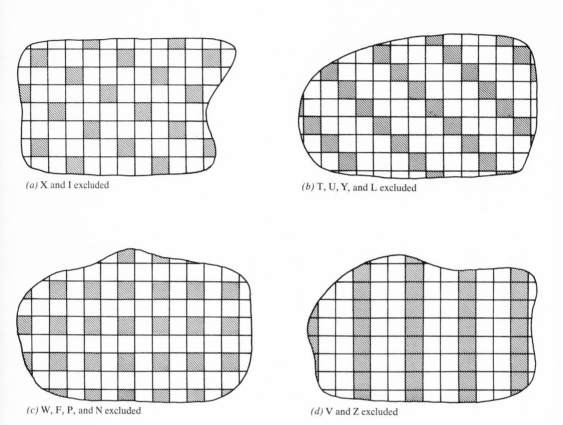

(a) X and I excluded

(b) T, U, Y, and L excluded

(c) W, F, P, and N excluded

(d) V and Z excluded

Figure 67. Repetitive patterns which exclude pentominoes from the infinite plane.

pentominoes from an *infinite* planar array of squares. Four configurations illustrate the minimal solutions for all the pentominoes. These are shown in Figure 67.

In Figure 67a, it is shown that only $\frac{1}{5}$ of the squares need be covered with monominoes to keep off the I and X pentominoes. In Figure 67b, $\frac{1}{4}$ of the squares must be covered to exclude the T, U, Y, and L pentominoes; as 67c shows, $\frac{1}{4}$ of the squares must also be covered to exclude the W, F, P,

54

and N pentominoes. Finally, in 67*d*, a full ⅓ of the squares are covered to exclude the V and Z pentominoes.

The methods used in this chapter involved the strenuous application of logic and ingenuity to the problems of excluding specified pentominoes with a minimum number of monominoes. However, there are other problems that resist solution by ingenuity but that can be solved, at least in principle, by examining all possible cases. Such a technique is described in the next chapter.

CHAPTER IV

Backtracking and Impossible Constructions

BACKTRACK PROGRAMMING

THE method of proof to demonstrate impossible constructions is an exhaustive search procedure called *backtrack*, the idea of which is to pursue each possible line of progress in turn until it leads either to success or to a blind alley. In the latter case, one then "backtracks" to the next possible procedure. After a preliminary discussion this technique will be applied to two very difficult pentomino problems.

Backtracking is illustrated conceptually by the maze-threading problem (Figure 68); the man in the maze (starting at X) adopts the escape strategy of running his right hand along the wall at all times; he follows the path indicated by the dots in Figure 68 until he is finally outside. The success of his strategy depends upon the construction of the maze walls. This incorporates the essential backtrack feature that

Figure 68. Escaping from a maze.

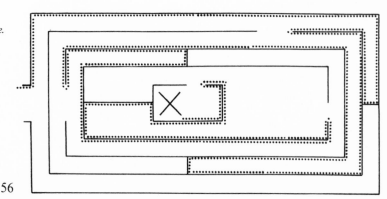

the same ground need not be searched repeatedly (a maze with the wrong wall connectivity will not yield to this method of solution); it also necessitates that the man recognize when he has finally succeeded. If he does not realize he has escaped, he will continue to follow his right hand along the doorjamb all the way around the *outside* wall of the building and back in the other side of the maze entrance.

Another example of backtrack programming is the classic combinatorial problem of placing 8 queens on the checkerboard so that no 2 can mutually "attack"; that is, no 2 can be in the same rank, file, or diagonal. Rather than examine *all* ways of placing 8 queens on the board (the number is a staggering 4,426,165,368, computed by a method explained in Chapter V), it suffices to restrict each queen to a single row of the board and to place them, 1 at a time, in unattacked squares. The first sequence of moves is shown in Figure 69*a*. To make the process converge fairly rapidly, the first queen is placed in a "typical" (middle) square of the first (bottom) row. The second queen is in the *first* (farthest right) available square of the second row, and the third queen is on the first available (unattacked) square of the third row. Similarly, the fourth queen is on the first (farthest right) available square of the fourth row, and similarly with the fifth queen on the fifth row and the sixth queen on the sixth row.

Now, however, there is no available square for a queen *anywhere* on the seventh row, so that it is necessary to "backtrack" to the position in Figure 69*b*. This can be "extended"

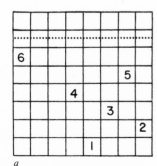

a

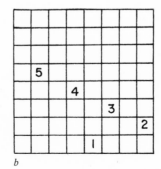

b

Figure 69. Backtrack programming for the 8-queen problem.

Figure 69 continued.

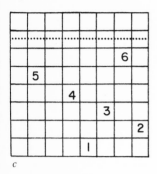

c

to the situation in Figure 69*c*. Now, however, there is no available square in the seventh row, and it is necessary to backtrack all the way to Figure 69*d*.

This can be extended to the situation in Figure 69*e*, but from this near miss one must retreat to Figure 69*f*, which can be extended to Figure 69*g*. From here it is necessary to backtrack to Figure 69*h*; advance can then be made to Figure 69*i*. Now it is necessary to go all the way back to the queen in the third row (Figure 69*j*). It has taken this long to establish that no solution exists with the first 3 queens as originally placed. Now, however, it is possible to advance, 1 queen at a time, all the way to the solution in Figure 69*m*.

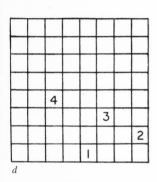

d

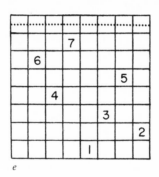

e

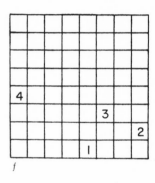

f

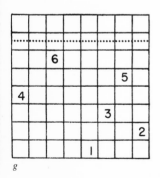

g

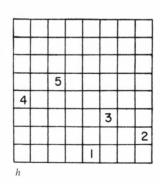

h

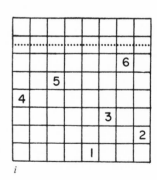

i

Figure 69 continued.

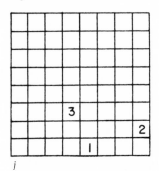

j

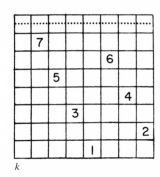

k

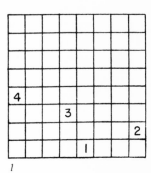

l

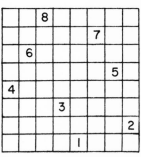

m

Although the path was somewhat laborious, it has led to success in an infinitesimal fraction of the time required to examine some 4 billion cases. Moreover, the backtracking procedure can be continued to determine all possible solutions in a reasonable length of time. The ambitious reader who wishes to attempt this should remember that 4 distinct locations for the *first* queen are involved if all solutions are to be found. The solution possessing the most symmetry is shown in Figure 70. There are 92 answers altogether, which reduce to 12 distinct cases if all rotations and reflections of the checkerboard are taken into account. In attempting to find all the solutions by backtrack, there is a considerable saving in time if these symmetries are accounted for in advance. Thus, after all answers have been found with the first queen located as in Figure 69*m*, no further partial solutions need be considered that have a queen on any edge 4 squares from any corner.

Although backtrack is not "elegant" in the way of a clever mathematical proof, it is an invaluable tool in the study of combinatorial problems. Moreover, the systematic pattern of advance and retreat until a solution is found, or the possibilities are exhausted so that the nonexistence of a solution is established, makes backtrack very well suited for the programming of an electronic digital computer. The digital

Figure 70. Most symmetrical solution to the 8-queen problem.

59

computer is programmed by transforming such a pattern into numerical form. The computer then, according to instructions, manipulates the numerical progression until a solution is found. Unlike a human problem solver, the modern digital computer does routine, repetitive calculations with incredible rapidity but fails to notice any shortcuts or patterns that had not already occurred to the programmer who gave the machine its detailed instructions. The challenge, then, is to formulate the question efficiently as a backtrack problem, after which the computer takes over the more tedious task of examining all the cases.

THE HERBERT TAYLOR CONFIGURATION

Impossibility proofs for Figure 71, the configuration proposed by the mathematician Herbert Taylor, now with North American Aviation, Downey, California, were discovered independently by John G. Fletcher of the University of California at Berkeley, and Spencer Earnshaw, at the time a student at Santa Monica City College in California. The proof presented here is a simplification of these two previous ones.

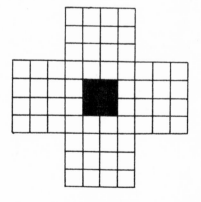

Figure 71. The Herbert Taylor Configuration.

Suppose it would be possible to cover the configuration of Figure 71 with the 12 distinct pentominoes. Then, at no stage along the way could a region of the "board" be isolated unless it contained a multiple of 5 squares. This will lead to a dead end.

First, consider the location of the X pentomino in the hypothetical covering. There are only 2 possibilities (ignoring positions symmetric to these as being equivalent), as shown in Figure 72.

In Case I, consider all possible locations for the I pentomino. No matter where it is placed, a region is isolated with a number of squares not a multiple of 5. Hence, Case I is a blind alley.

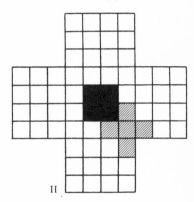

Figure 72. The 2 possible locations for the X in the Herbert Taylor Configuration.

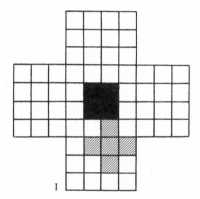

In Case II, there are 2 inequivalent locations for the I pentomino that leave the remaining regions with numbers of squares divisible by 5, as shown in Figure 73.

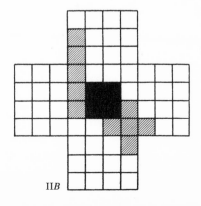

Figure 73. The 2 possible locations for the I in Case II.

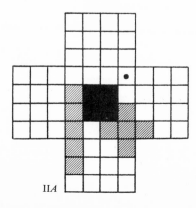

In Case IIA, consider the possible ways the pentomino covering the "dotted" square might enter the "east wing" of the figure. There are 3 distinguishable situations (Figure 74).

In Case IIA 1, the south and east wings are congruent, and either can be filled by the P and L pentominoes or by the W and Y pentominoes, but in no other way. Thus P, L, W, and Y must be used (for example, as in Figure 75), and the pentomino covering the dot is either the N or the V. However, a search for a place to put the T pentomino leads only to the location shown in Figure 75, which also necessitates that the V cover the dot. Now, however, the P pentomino is needed next to the T, but it has already been used. Thus Case IIA 1 is eliminated. (The numbers on the pentominoes in Figure 75 refer to the order in which they were placed on the "board.")

Figure 74. The 3 ways to cover the "dotted" square of Case IIA.

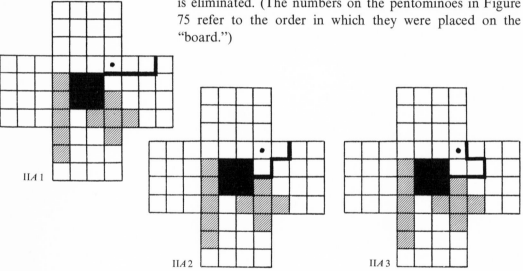

IIA 1

IIA 2

IIA 3

Figure 75. Exploring Case IIA 1.

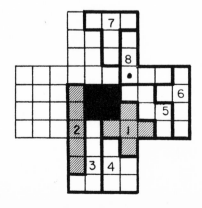

In Case IIA 2, the south wing, as before, can contain either the pair P and L or the pair W and Y; while the east wing can contain either W and P or L and P. The only consistent choice for *both* regions is W, Y in the south and L, P in the east (see Figure 76). The pentomino covering the dot must be the F, in either of 2 orientations. Next, the N pentomino can be consistently fitted only as shown (Figure 76), and there remains no consistent location for the T pentomino, thus eliminating Case IIA 2.

Figure 76. Exploring Case IIA 2.

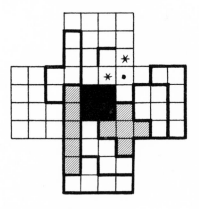

In Case IIA 3, the south wing again may contain either the pair P, L or the pair W, Y, while the east wing may contain either V, F or U, L. Next, there are 4 possibilities for the T pentomino (avoiding obvious dead ends), as shown in Figure 77. In IIA 3a, the dotted square and the neighboring asterisked ones cannot be extended to form a pentomino, because W already has been used, and N would isolate a block of 2 squares. In IIA 3b, the N must be used to cover the dot, and there remains no consistent location for the Z. For IIA 3c, the L must cover the dot, and then the square to the left of the dot cannot be covered. In IIA 3d, whether V, F, or U, L are chosen to cover the east wing, only Z can be used to cover the dot, and the construction clearly cannot be completed. Thus IIA 3 is impossible, which completes the elimination of Case IIA.

63

Figure 77. The 4 possible locations
for the T in Case IIA 3.

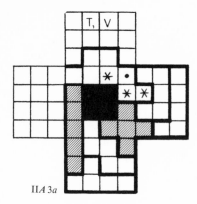

IIA 3a

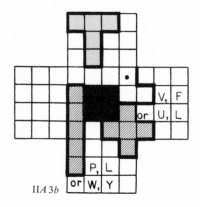

IIA 3b

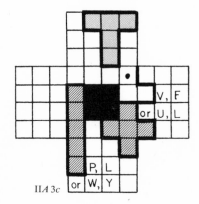

IIA 3c

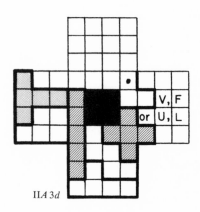

IIA 3d

Case II*B* remains. Here, there are exactly 4 possible locations for the N pentomino, as shown in Figure 78. In II*B* 1,
the only consistent location for the T pentomino is as shown

*Figure 78. The 4 locations for the N in Case II*B.

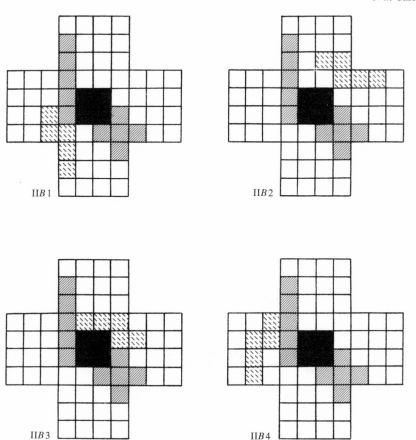

IIB1

IIB2

IIB3

IIB4

in Figure 79. The north wing can then be completed only
by use of the P pentomino. Without the P, the south wing
must be filled in with W, Y and the west wing with V, Z. The
asterisked square of Figure 79 cannot then be covered by any
remaining pentomino, which settles case II*B* 1.

65

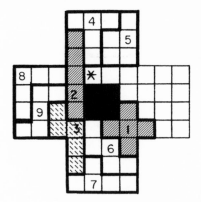

Figure 79. The only position for
the T in Case IIB 1.

For II*B* 2, the north wing must be filled with U, L, and
(since L is no longer available) the east wing must contain
W, Y. The only consistent location for the T pentomino is
then in the west wing (see Figure 80), after which the Z pentomino will not fit anywhere. Thus Case II*B* 2 is also
eliminated.

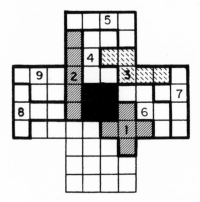

Figure 80. The only consistent
location for the T in Case IIB 2.

In II*B* 3, the east wing may be occupied either by U, L or
F, V; and the north wing by U, Y or P, T (see Figure 81). (If
P is used in the north wing with V, Y, Z, or L, then there is no
suitable location left for the T.)

In Case II*B* 3*a*, the only consistent location for the T pentomino is in the west wing (see Figure 82), which then leaves
no legitimate position for the Z. Considering II*B* 3*b*, there

Figure 81. The U and Y or the P and T must be used to fill the north wing in Case IIB 3.

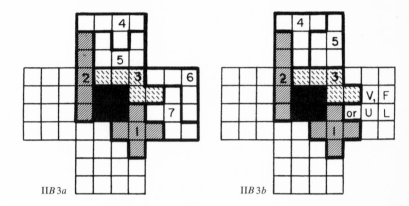

IIB 3a   IIB 3b

Figure 82. Elimination of Case IIB 3a.

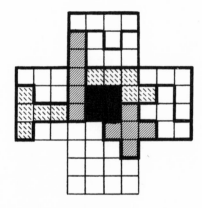

are 2 possible locations for the Z pentomino, as shown in Figure 83. In IIB 3*bi*, there is no region left where the W pentomino will fit. In Case IIB 3*bii*, the location of the Z requires the V in the west wing, leaving U, L to fill the east

Figure 83. The 2 possibilities for locating the Z in Case IIB 3b.

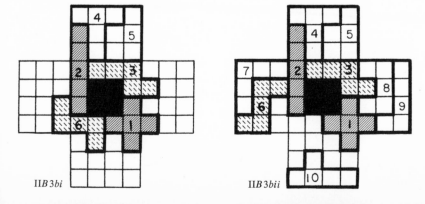

IIB 3bi   IIB 3bii

wing. There is only 1 location left for the Y pentomino, as shown, after which the F pentomino does not fit at all. This eliminates Case II*B*3*b*, which completes Case II*B*3.

Finally, Case II*B*4 is eliminated by observing that the T must be placed in the north wing, above the I, which forces the P next to the T and the Y underneath; the east wing cannot now be filled. This completes Case II*B*, completing Case II, and answering the original question of the existence of a pentomino covering for Figure 71 in the negative. A schematic diagram of the cases and subcases just considered is given in Figure 84.

Figure 84. Branches used in the impossibility proof.

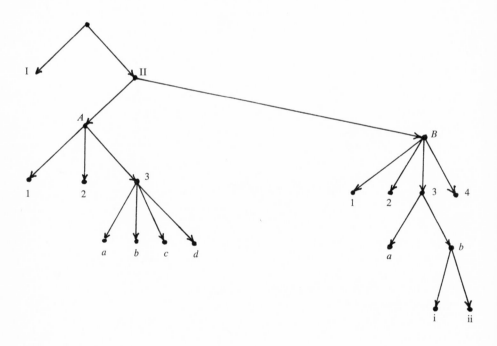

A backtrack "solution" to the "jagged square" proposed by R. M. Robinson (Figure 85) was also discovered by Spencer Earnshaw. It is even longer and more intricate than the preceding solution and will only be sketched briefly here, in 8 steps.

Figure 85. R. M. Robinson's jagged square.

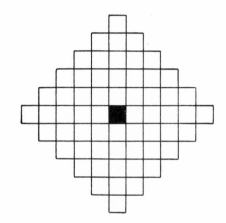

1. Only 8 of the 12 pentominoes (W, X, Y, F, I, L, P, N) can possibly occupy "corners" in Figure 85.

2. There are 70 ways $\left(\dfrac{8!}{4!\ 4!} = 70\right)$ to select 4 of these pentominoes to fill the 4 corners. (The formula for the number of ways to select 8 things, 4 at a time, comes from Theorem 4 in Chapter V. The meaning of the symbol "*n!*", called *n factorial*, is explained in the statement of Theorem 2 in Chapter V.) The following table gives the maximum number of edge squares (*not* including corner squares) each pentomino can occupy when it is and when it is not a corner piece. For each set of corner pieces, the corresponding maximum number of coverable edges is obtained readily from the table on page 70.

69

Pentomino	Corner Squares	Maximum Number of Edge Squares
W	1	2
	0	3
X	1	2
	0	2
Y	1	1
	0	2
F	1	2
	0	2
I	1	0
	0	1
L	1	0
	0	1
P	1	1
	0	2
N	1	1
	0	2
T	0	1
U	0	1
V	0	1
Z	0	1

3. In Figure 86, the 4 kinds of squares of Figure 85 are depicted clearly. Topologically, the corner squares, edge squares, and interior-boundary squares, all taken together, form the "total boundary" of the configuration, and the basic idea of Earnshaw's solution is to relate coverings to this "total boundary" of 24 squares.

Specifically, there are only 4 pentominoes (V, Z, I, and L) that can occupy an interior-boundary square and also cover their maximum number of edge or corner squares simultaneously.

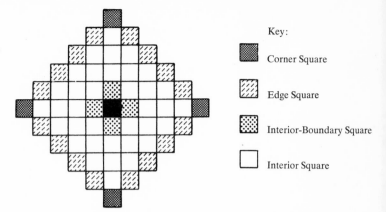

Figure 86. Identification of corner, edge, interior-boundary, and interior squares.

Key:

■ Corner Square

▨ Edge Square

▦ Interior-Boundary Square

□ Interior Square

4. The V and I pentominoes cannot simultaneously occupy both an edge or corner square and an interior-boundary square without violating the *multiple-of-5* rule for the remaining regions; this rule requires that the number of squares in an isolated region must be a multiple of 5 in order for that region to be exactly coverable by pentominoes. This is illustrated in Figure 87; the I pentomino has been placed in its 2 representative locations, and the various inequivalent positions of the V pentomino occupying both an edge and an interior-boundary point are shown. In all 16 cases, the multiple-of-5 rule is violated.

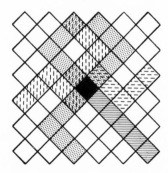

Figure 87. The 16 ways for the V and I simultaneously to occupy an edge or corner square and an interior-boundary square all violate the "multiple-of-5" rule.

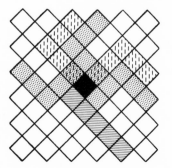

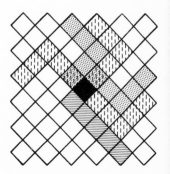

5. There are 15 remaining ways of selecting 2 from the V, Z, I, and L pentominoes to cover both an edge or corner and an interior-boundary square to be studied. (There are 6 ways to select 2 of these 4 pieces, and, in general, several ways of placing the selected pair on the "board.") A preliminary count of boundary squares shows that 1 of these situations would have to occur. However, it is found that only the pair I, Z has any hope of success.

6. The cases where I and Z each cover both an edge or corner square and an interior-boundary square are studied. Numerous side results (for example, that F and X are 2 of the 4 corner pieces) are obtained from this study. Finally, it is shown that I and Z must cover exactly 1 interior-boundary square and 1 edge or corner square, while another piece (either T, V, or L) covers the remaining 2 interior-boundary squares.

7. The assumption that the V covers the remaining 2 interior-boundary squares (see Figure 88) leads in all cases to a contradiction.

8. If V is *not* used as the piece covering the remaining 2 interior-boundary points, contradictions are also reached. This step concludes the impossibility proof associated with Figure 85.

The reader is invited to attempt to put the flesh on the very meager skeleton of the proof that has just been given. Even more significantly, he is encouraged to discover a shorter procedure for arriving at the same conclusion.

Figure 88. The V cannot cover the remaining 2 interior-boundary squares.

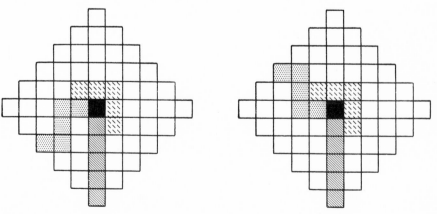

Figure 88 continued.

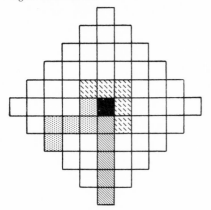

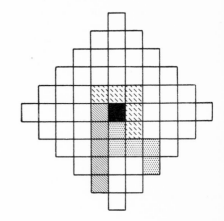

Figure 89. A solution to a close approximation of the jagged-square problem.

Figure 90. The jagged square can be filled with pentominoes if the hole is moved to the edge.

Even if the monomino is moved to another interior location, no solution to placing the 12 pentominoes on the remaining 60 squares has been found. The closest approximation known to the original pattern is the one given in Figure 89.

A near solution to the jagged-square construction has been discovered by the recreational-mathematics fan J. A. Lindon of Surrey, England. In it, the monomino has been moved from the center to the edge (Figure 90).

73

CHAPTER V

Some Theorems about Counting

IT HAS often been said that the most basic of all mathematical operations is *counting,* and the late great German mathematician Hermann Weyl once wrote that underlying almost all mathematical identities is the principle that if an enumeration of the same objects is performed in two different ways, the results must be equal.

Throughout earlier chapters, questions have arisen as to the number of ways certain objects can be fitted into specified "containers," or patterns. There are also frequent questions in this book, and in mathematics generally, involving how many objects with certain specified characteristics exist, and involving problems of determining the number of configurations and patterns of a particular type. All of these are *finite enumeration* problems, and, like combinatorial geometry, with which this book is primarily concerned, they belong to a branch of mathematics called *combinatorial analysis,* which is the study of combinations of numbers or quantities of things. The ever-increasing importance of digital computers in modern technology has revived a widespread interest in combinatorial analysis, a subject that also has had important applications in such modern scientific fields as circuit design, coded communications, traffic control, crystallography, and probability theory.

The present chapter is intended to serve as an introduction to combinatorial analysis and, particularly, that part of the field concerned with *enumeration* (that is, counting). This material, while it is more difficult and requires greater concentration than that of earlier sections, will serve not only to enhance the reader's understanding and appreciation of the remainder of the book, but also to give him some facility in the formulation and solution of such problems wherever they may be encountered. However, for those who wish to concentrate on the recreational aspect of polyominoes, this chapter can be skipped and the rest of the book enjoyed without it.

COMBINATIONS

There are 10 ways to pick a number from 0 through 9. There are $10^2 = 100$ ways to pick a *pair* of numbers, each digit one of the numerals from 0 through 9, since these pairs may be regarded as the numbers 00, 01, 02, 03, ..., 97, 98, 99. Similarly, there are $10^3 = 1,000$ ways to pick a *triple* of numbers, each digit again one of the numerals from 0 through 9, since the triples may be regarded as all the numbers from 000 to 999. In general, there are 10^n ways to pick an n-tuple of numbers, each digit a number from 0 to 9. In fact, there are 10^n ways to pick an n-tuple of *symbols* from some set of 10 distinct symbols, since it is only a matter of nomenclature as to whether the symbols are called 0, 1, 2, ..., 9; $A, B, C, ..., J$; $a_1, a_2, a_3, ..., a_{10}$; or anything else.

If the basic *set,* or group of symbols from which the n-tuple is to be picked, consists of k symbols, and an ordered sequence of length n is formed—where each symbol can be any one of the k basic symbols—there are k^n such n-tuples. If the basic symbols are 0 and 1, and all possible sequences of length 4 are to be formed, $n = 4$ and $k = 2$, so that there are $k^n = 2^4 = 16$ such sequences. These combinations can be used to represent the decimal-system numbers from 0 to 15 (to the left of the equal signs in the table below) in the binary number system, which is based on the two digits 0 and 1 and used in computer mathematics, as follows:

$0 = 0000$	$4 = 0100$	$8 = 1000$	$12 = 1100$
$1 = 0001$	$5 = 0101$	$9 = 1001$	$13 = 1101$
$2 = 0010$	$6 = 0110$	$10 = 1010$	$14 = 1110$
$3 = 0011$	$7 = 0111$	$11 = 1011$	$15 = 1111$

A still more general formulation about combinations is the following theorem.

Theorem 1. Suppose there are n sets, where the first set contains k_1 objects, the second set contains k_2 objects, and so on, with the n-th set containing k_n objects. The number of different sequences of n objects, with the first object chosen from the first set, the second object from the second set, and so on, with the n-th object from the n-th set, is the product $k_1 k_2 \ldots k_n$. (In particular, if all n sets of objects are the same, then $k_1 = k_2 \ldots = k_n = k$, and the number of combinations is k^n.)

Proof. An object may be picked from the first set in any of k_1 ways. For each choice an object may be picked from the second set in k_2 ways, giving $k_1 k_2$ ways to make a selection from the first 2 sets. For each of these $k_1 k_2$ selections, an object may be picked from the third set in any of k_3 ways, giving $k_1 k_2 k_3$ ways to make the selection from the first 3 sets. Proceeding in this fashion, there are $k_1 k_2 k_3 \ldots k_n$ ways to make a selection from each of the n sets.

As an illustration of Theorem 1, the automobile registration plates in a hypothetical state consist of 2 letters (from the standard 26-letter alphabet), followed by 4 numerals (from the usual set of 10). Then the number of possible license plates in that state is $26 \cdot 26 \cdot 10 \cdot 10 \cdot 10 \cdot 10 = 6{,}760{,}000$ (the dots between the numerals are equivalent to multiplication signs).

A more difficult question is the number of *unordered* combinations of n symbols from a basic "alphabet" of k symbols. By an unordered combination, it is meant that the order in which the n symbols are arranged is to be disregarded. For example, if 4 symbols are taken from the binary number system, which consists of only the two digits 0 and 1, but no attention is paid to order, there are only 5 distinct cases:

namely, 0000, 0001, 0011, 0111, and 1111. This contrasts with the 16 distinct *ordered* cases previously listed. When 2 identical dice are thrown, the number of distinguishable configurations is not 36, but only 21, since, for example, (1, 4) and (4, 1) are not distinguishable. (Of course, there are only 11 different possible dice *totals,* these being the 11 numbers from 2 to 12 inclusive. However, the total of 7, for example, is achieved in 3 distinguishable ways, as $3 + 4$, $2 + 5$, and $1 + 6$.) The solution to the problem of counting the number of unordered combinations will be reserved until the next section, since additional concepts must first be introduced.

EXERCISES

1. In a typical 7-digit telephone number, the first 2 digits are chosen from 2 through 9 inclusive, while the remaining 5 digits can be any number from 1 to 0 inclusive. How many possible telephone numbers are there? (NOTE: *The answers to all Exercises in this chapter will be found in Appendix I, pages 139–144.*)

2. There are 6 classes in a country school, with 12 students in the first grade, 15 in the second, 9 in the third, 13 in the fourth, 11 in the fifth, and 12 in the sixth grades. One student from each class is to be appointed to the safety committee. In how many ways can this committee be constituted?

PERMUTATIONS, FACTORIALS, AND BINOMIAL COEFFICIENTS

A set of k distinct objects is given, and a first object, a second object, and finally a k-th object are to be picked from it. In how many ways can this be done? For example, in how many different orders can a deck of 52 cards be dealt out; and in how many distinct ways can the letters A, B, C, D, E be arranged? The answer is given by the following theorem.

Theorem 2. The number of different ways in which k objects can be assigned an *ordering* (that is, first, second, third, through k-th) is the product $1 \cdot 2 \cdot 3 \cdots (k - 1) \cdot k$.   77

(This product is denoted by $k!$, and, as mentioned earlier, is called *k factorial*.)

Proof. The choice of the first object can be made in k ways. This leaves $k - 1$ possibilities for the second object, $k - 2$ choices for the third, and so on. Hence, the complete ordering can be done in exactly $k(k - 1)(k - 2)\cdots 2 \cdot 1 = k!$ distinct ways.

In the chart below are the values of $k!$ for $k = 1$ through 20.

k	$k!$	k	$k!$
1	1	11	39,916,800
2	2	12	479,001,600
3	6	13	6,227,020,800
4	24	14	87,178,291,200
5	120	15	1,307,674,368,000
6	720	16	20,922,789,888,000
7	5,040	17	355,687,428,096,000
8	40,320	18	6,402,373,705,728,000
9	362,880	19	121,645,100,408,832,000
10	3,628,800	20	2,432,902,008,176,640,000

Since $3! = 6$, there are 6 ways to arrange the letters A, E, T; namely, AET, ATE, EAT, ETA, TAE, TEA. Similarly, there are $5! = 120$ ways to arrange the letters A, B, C, D, and E to form "words." The reader may find it amusing to look for sets of k letters whose permutations include as many English words as possible, for $k = 2$, 3, 4, 5, and 6. For $k = 4$, it is difficult to find sets where more than 5 of the 24 possible permutations are English words; and for $k = 5$, 8 English words among the 120 permutations is an excellent score.

In general, $(k + 1)k! = (k + 1)!$, since the product of all the numbers from 1 through k, multiplied by $k + 1$, is the product of all the numbers from 1 through $k + 1$. This gives the relation

$$k! = \frac{(k + 1)!}{k + 1},$$

and if $k = 0$, $0! = \frac{1!}{1} = 1$, which is generally adopted as the definition of *zero factorial*. (The original definition did not cover $k = 0$, so that this extends it.)

A famous approximate formula for $k!$ called *Stirling's formula* is:

$$k! \sim \sqrt{2\pi k}\left(\frac{k}{e}\right)^k.$$

Here π (pi) $= 3.14159 \ldots$ is the ratio of the circumference to the diameter of a circle, and $e = 2.71828 \ldots$ is another famous mathematical constant. (It is the base of "natural logarithms.") The sign $\sqrt{}$ is read as "the square root of"; and the sign $\sim$, which is read "is *asymptotic* to," means that the ratio of the 2 sides gets closer and closer to 1 as k gets larger and larger. For any specific choice of k, an *approximate* value for $k!$ is found, and the approximation becomes better and better, on a percentage basis, as larger and larger values of k are chosen. The derivation of Stirling's formula is completely outside the range of combinatorial analysis, and will not be given here. However, to get an approximate answer to the number of ways in which a deck of 52 cards can be dealt out, in Stirling's formula ($k = 52$).

$$52! \approx \sqrt{104\pi}\left(\frac{52}{e}\right)^{52} \approx 18.076 \, (19.130)^{52} \approx 8.054 \times 10^{67}$$

is obtained, where $\approx$ means "approximately equal to." For numbers that are so huge, it is frequently unimportant to know the exact digits, and an approximation is sufficient.

Suppose that a set of k distinct objects is given and that only r of them are to be selected; these will be labeled first, second, and so on, through r-th. The number of distinct ways of selecting such an ordered subset of r objects from a set of k objects will be denoted by $(k)_r$.

Theorem 3.

$$(k)_r = \frac{k!}{(k-r)!} = k(k-1)(k-2)\cdots(k-r+1).$$

Proof. The first object may be selected in k ways, the second object in $k-1$ ways, and in general the j-th object in $k-j+1$ ways. In particular, the r-th and final object can be selected in $k-r+1$ ways; thus, there are $k(k-1)(k-2)\cdots(k-r+1)$ choices altogether. Since this is the product of the numbers from 1 to k *except* for the numbers from 1 to $k-r$, it equals $\frac{k!}{(k-r)!}$.

EXERCISES

3. In a certain contest, 3 distinct letters of the alphabet must be selected and written down in the right order. There is only 1 way to win. How many ways are there to lose?

4. Each of 6 players is dealt 1 card from a deck of 52 distinct cards. How many different situations (combinations of people and cards) may result?

When 5 cards are dealt to a player from a deck of 52 cards, he looks at his "hand" without regard to the *order* in which the cards were dealt. That is, the number of possible "poker hands" is the number of ways of selecting an unordered subset of 5 cards from the 52-card deck. Similarly, the number of possible "bridge hands" is the number of ways of selecting an unordered subset of 13 cards from the 52-card deck. In general, if there is a set of k distinct objects, and r of them are to be selected, the number of possible unordered subsets of

80 r objects from the set of k objects will be denoted by $\binom{k}{r}$.

Theorem 4.

$$\binom{k}{r} = \frac{k(k-1)(k-2)\cdots(k-r+1)}{r(r-1)(r-2)\cdots 2\cdot 1} = \frac{k_r}{r!} = \frac{k!}{r!(k-r)!}.$$

Proof. The number of *ordered* subsets of r objects from a set of k objects is $(k)_r$. Given these r objects, they could be arranged in any of $r!$ distinct permuted orders and still constitute the same *unordered subset.* Thus, the number of unordered subsets is $\frac{(k)_r}{r!}$. From Theorem 3, this is also equal to

$$\frac{k!}{r!(k-r)!} \text{ and to } \frac{k(k-1)(k-2)\cdots(k-r+1)}{r(r-1)(r-2)\cdots 2\cdot 1}.$$

By Theorem 4, the number of possible poker hands is

$$\binom{52}{5} = \frac{52\cdot 51\cdot 50\cdot 49\cdot 48}{5\cdot 4\cdot 3\cdot 2\cdot 1} = 2{,}598{,}960;$$

while the number of possible bridge hands is

$$\binom{52}{13} = \frac{52\cdot 51\cdot 50\cdot 49\cdot 48\cdot 47\cdot 46\cdot 45\cdot 44\cdot 43\cdot 42\cdot 41\cdot 40}{13\cdot 12\cdot 11\cdot 10\cdot 9\cdot 8\cdot 7\cdot 6\cdot 5\cdot 4\cdot 3\cdot 2\cdot 1} = 635{,}013{,}559{,}600.$$

EXERCISES

5. In how many ways can 4 monominoes be placed on an 8×8 chessboard?

6. In how many ways can 8 queens be placed on an 8×8 chessboard?

7. In how many ways can 6 pentominoes be chosen from the set of 12 distinct pentominoes?

8. A club wishes to hold meetings 3 evenings a week. How many possible choices are there for the nights on which meetings are to be held?

81

POLYOMINOES

The *binomial theorem* of algebra is the formula

$$(x + y)^k = x^k + \binom{k}{1}x^{k-1}y + \binom{k}{2}x^{k-2}y^2 + \binom{k}{3}x^{k-3}y^3 + \cdots + \binom{k}{k-1}xy^{k-1} + y^k.$$

For this reason, the numbers $\binom{k}{r}$ are known as the *binomial coefficients;* a coefficient is a multiplier, or factor, in mathematical operations. Often, $\binom{k}{r}$ is read as "the binomial coefficient k over r." The reader is encouraged to try to prove the binomial theorem from what he has already learned about binomial coefficients.

While the number of subsets containing *no* objects from a set of k objects has not been discussed, the convention that there is 1 such empty subset, which agrees with $\binom{k}{0} = \frac{k!}{0!\,k!} = 1$ will be adopted. In the binomial theorem, the initial term x^k may thus be regarded as having the coefficient $\binom{k}{0}$, while the final term y^k has the coefficient $\binom{k}{k}$.

The eighteenth-century French mathematician Blaise Pascal arranged the binomial coefficients into the following triangle:

$$\binom{0}{0}$$

$$\binom{1}{0} \quad \binom{1}{1}$$

$$\binom{2}{0} \quad \binom{2}{1} \quad \binom{2}{2}$$

$$\binom{3}{0} \quad \binom{3}{1} \quad \binom{3}{2} \quad \binom{3}{3}$$

$$\binom{4}{0} \quad \binom{4}{1} \quad \binom{4}{2} \quad \binom{4}{3} \quad \binom{4}{4}$$

82

and so on.

This array is known as Pascal's triangle, and the explicit numerical values are shown below.

$$
\begin{array}{ccccccccccccccccc}
 & & & & & & & & 1 & & & & & & & & \\
 & & & & & & & 1 & & 1 & & & & & & & \\
 & & & & & & 1 & & 2 & & 1 & & & & & & \\
 & & & & & 1 & & 3 & & 3 & & 1 & & & & & \\
 & & & & 1 & & 4 & & 6 & & 4 & & 1 & & & & \\
 & & & 1 & & 5 & & 10 & & 10 & & 5 & & 1 & & & \\
 & & 1 & & 6 & & 15 & & 20 & & 15 & & 6 & & 1 & & \\
 & 1 & & 7 & & 21 & & 35 & & 35 & & 21 & & 7 & & 1 & \\
1 & & 8 & & 28 & & 56 & & 70 & & 56 & & 28 & & 8 & & 1
\end{array}
$$

and so on.

Since the time of Pascal, literally hundreds of identities concerning this numerical triangle have been proved. Here are some for the reader to try.

1. The sums of the rows are the successive powers of 2. That is,

$$
\binom{k}{0} + \binom{k}{1} + \binom{k}{2} + \cdots + \binom{k}{k} = 2^k.
$$

2. The alternating sums of the rows (that is, the first term minus the second term plus the third term minus the fourth term, and so on) are all *zero* except for the top row, thus,

$$
\binom{k}{0} - \binom{k}{1} + \binom{k}{2} - \binom{k}{3} \pm \cdots \pm \binom{k}{k} = 0.
$$

3. Every entry is the sum of the 2 entries approximately above it (northeast and northwest of it, so to speak). That is,

$$
\binom{k}{r} = \binom{k-1}{r-1} + \binom{k-1}{r}.
$$

4. Each row is symmetric. That is, $\binom{k}{r} = \binom{k}{k-r}$.

83

5. The sum of the squares across any row equals the middle entry in the row twice as far down, excluding the top row. That is,

$$\binom{k}{0}^2 + \binom{k}{1}^2 + \binom{k}{2}^2 + \binom{k}{3}^2 + \cdots + \binom{k}{k}^2 = \binom{2k}{k}.$$

It is now possible to answer a question raised earlier: namely, what is the number of unordered combinations of n symbols from a basic alphabet of k symbols?

Theorem 5. The number of possible unordered combinations of n selections from a basic alphabet of k symbols is

$$\binom{k + n - 1}{n} = \binom{k + n - 1}{k - 1}.$$

Proof. First, to illustrate the method of proof, a typical unordered combination of $n = 7$ selections from an alphabet of $k = 4$ symbols will be used, the symbols being a, b, c, d. If the combination is $c\, a\, d\, b\, a\, a\, b$, it is written in the "standardized form" $a\, a\, a \mid b\, b \mid c \mid d$. Since *unordered* combinations are being studied, the standardized form is the same unordered combination as the original. In general, an unordered combination is put into standardized form by arranging all the occurrences of the first symbol together at the beginning, then a vertical demarcation line, then all occurrences of the second symbol, and so on. If one of the four alphabet symbols fails to occur, the vertical demarcation line for it is nevertheless indicated. In this way, there are always n alphabetic symbols in the standardized form, and $k - 1$ vertical demarcation lines. With both alphabetic symbols and demarcation lines classified as *marks,* one gets a total of $n + k - 1$ marks. In the illustrative example, there are $7 + 4 - 1 = 10$ marks. The specification of *which* $k - 1$ of a string of $n + k - 1$ marks are to be demarcation lines is *equivalent* to writing down an unordered combination of n selections from a k-symbol alphabet in standardized form. For example, if in the sequence of 10 marks, $- - - - - - - - - -$, it is specified that the fourth, seventh, and ninth are to be demarcation lines, the result is $- - -\mid- -\mid-\mid-$, which is automatically filled in as $a\,a\,a\,|\,b\,b\,|\,c\,|\,d$. Demarcation lines specified at the first, fourth, and fifth places give $|--||-----$, which would correspond to $|b\,b|\,|d\,d\,d\,d\,d$, and similarly, every choice of locations for the demarcation lines is a *different* unordered combination in standard form. By Theorem 4, there are exactly $\binom{n+k-1}{k-1}$ ways to select $k-1$ of the $n+k-1$ marks to be the demarcation lines, and this is therefore the number of unordered combinations of n objects selected from a k-symbol alphabet. Finally,

$$\binom{n+k-1}{k-1} = \frac{(n+k-1)!}{(k-1)!\,n!} = \binom{n+k-1}{n}.$$

EXAMPLES

1. The number of unordered combinations of 5 selections from the binary digits is $\binom{5+2-1}{5} = \binom{6}{5} = 6$. In standardized form, these are $0\,0\,0\,0\,0\,|\,,\,0\,0\,0\,0\,|\,1\,,\,0\,0\,0\,|\,1\,1\,,\,0\,0\,|\,1\,1\,1\,,\,0\,|\,1\,1\,1\,1$, and $|\,1\,1\,1\,1\,1$. Each of these unordered combinations corresponds to one or more ordered combinations, as shown below. Two ordered combinations correspond to the same unordered combination if they have the same number of 1's.

Unordered Combination	Ordered Combinations
00000	00000
00001	00001, 00010, 00100, 01000, 10000
00011	00011, 00101, 01001, 10001, 00110,
	01010, 10010, 01100, 10100, 11000
00111	00111, 01011, 10011, 01101, 10101,
	11001, 01110, 10110, 11010, 11100
01111	01111, 10111, 11011, 11101, 11110
11111	11111

Note that the sizes of these 6 categories of ordered combinations are the numbers 1, 5, 10, 10, 5, 1, which form a row of Pascal's triangle.

85

2. The number of unordered combinations of 3 selections from a 3-symbol alphabet is $\binom{3 + 3 - 1}{3} = \binom{5}{3} = 10$. Specifically, they are $a\,a\,a$, $a\,a\,b$, $a\,a\,c$, $a\,b\,b$, $a\,b\,c$, $a\,c\,c$, $b\,b\,b$, $b\,b\,c$, $b\,c\,c$, $c\,c\,c$.

EXERCISES

9. Determine the number of unordered combinations of 4 selections from a 5-symbol alphabet, and list them.

10. A mixed assortment of fruit, consisting of apples, oranges, and pears, is on sale for a dollar per dozen. How many distinct assortments might a customer get for his dollar?

11. Given, k symbols of r distinct types. There are k_1 of the first type, k_2 of the second type, k_3 of the third type, $\ldots$, and k_r of the r-th type. (Of course, $k_1 + k_2 + k_3 + \cdots + k_r = k$.) Show that the number of distinguishable permutations of these k symbols is

$$\frac{k!}{k_1!\,k_2!\,k_3\cdots k_r!}$$

12. Use the result of the previous exercise to compute the number of distinct permutations of PEPPER and of MISSISSIPPI.

INCLUSION AND EXCLUSION

There is an ancient "folk theorem" asserting that a horse has at least 12 legs, because it has 2 legs in front, 2 in back, 2 on each side, 1 at each corner, and that doesn't even take into account the ones at the bottom!

A similar "paradox" is designed to prove that there are no workdays in the business year. Of the 365 days, 104 are weekends, 7 are paid holidays, and 10 are paid vacation. Moreover, $\frac{1}{3}$ of the day, or 122 days a year, is spent sleeping, and still another $\frac{1}{3}$ of the day (another 122 days a year) lies outside the 8-hour workday. This gives $104 + 7 + 10 + 122 + 122 = 365$ days a year *not* devoted to work.

It is obvious that the resolution of these paradoxes involves the fact that there are "overlaps" in the categories considered for which proper accounting must be made. Thus, some of the horse's front legs may be on the right side and some of the corner legs may also be on the bottom. Similarly, some of the 8 hours a day spent sleeping occur on weekends and holidays and should not be subtracted twice from the 365-day year. What is remarkable is that there is a very simple formula, known as the "principle of inclusion and exclusion" (and also known as the "principle of cross-classification") that gives the correct answers to problems of this type by taking into precise account the amount of overlap.

Theorem 6. In a set of N objects, suppose N_1 of them have a property P_1, N_2 of them have a property P_2, and so on, and N_r of them have a property P_r. Then the number of objects having *none* of the properties $P_1, P_2, \ldots, P_r$ is N_0, given by

$$N_0 = N - (N_1 + N_2 + \cdots + N_r) + (N_{1,2} + N_{1,3}$$
$$+ \cdots + N_{2,3} + \cdots + N_{r-1,r}) - (N_{1,2,3} + N_{1,2,4}$$
$$+ \cdots + N_{r-2,r-1,r}) + - \cdots \pm (N_{1,2,3} \cdots {}_r),$$

where $N_{i,j,\ldots,m}$ is the number of objects having all the properties $P_i, P_j, \ldots, P_m$.

Illustration. Let $N = 365$ days, and let $P_1 = $ weekends, $P_2 = $ paid holidays, $P_3 = $ paid vacation, $P_4 = $ sleep time, and $P_5 = $ the time that is spent neither working nor sleeping. Then, in days, $N_1 = 104$, $N_2 = 7$, $N_3 = 10$, $N_4 = 122$, and $N_5 = 122$. However, $N_{1,4} = \frac{104}{3}$, $N_{2,4} = \frac{7}{3}$, $N_{3,4} = \frac{10}{3}$, $N_{1,5} = \frac{104}{3}$, $N_{2,5} = \frac{7}{3}$, and $N_{3,5} = \frac{10}{3}$. All the other $N_{i,j,\ldots,m}$ are zero. Hence, N_0, the time actually worked, is

$$N_0 = N - (N_1 + N_2 + N_3 + N_4 + N_5)$$
$$+ (N_{1,4} + N_{2,4} + N_{3,4} + N_{1,5} + N_{2,5} + N_{3,5})$$
$$= 365 - 365 + \frac{242}{3} = 80\tfrac{2}{3} \text{ days} = 1,936 \text{ hours} = 48.4 \text{ 40-hour weeks.}$$

Proof. From the set of N objects, we subtract the N_1 that have property P_1, the N_2 that have property P_2, and so on. However, the objects that have 2 such properties have been subtracted *twice*, and must therefore be restored *once*, so that   87 all terms $N_{i,j}$ are added back in. The objects that have 3 of the basic properties, say P_i, P_j, and P_k, have now been subtracted 3 times by $-N_i - N_j - N_k$, and added back 3 times by $+N_{i,j} + N_{i,k} + N_{j,k}$, and must therefore be subtracted out once more, so that all terms $N_{i,j,k}$ must be *subtracted*. In general, an object with t of the r properties will be subtracted out t times, added back $\binom{t}{2}$ times, subtracted again $\binom{t}{3}$ times, added again $\binom{t}{4}$ times, and so on, for a net contribution of $-t + \binom{t}{2} - \binom{t}{3} + \binom{t}{4} - + \cdots \pm \binom{t}{t}$, which is 1 less than $1 - \binom{t}{1} + \binom{t}{2} - \binom{t}{3} + - \cdots \pm \binom{t}{t} = 0$. That is, an object with 1 or more of the specified r properties will be subtracted out exactly once.

EXAMPLES

1. A fisherman wishes to fish in the $1,000 \times 1,500$ mile area shown in Figure 91. However, he must stay out of the 3 square test areas A, B, C, as shown, each of which is 500 miles on a side, and the centers of any 2 of which are 400 miles apart. How many square miles remain in which he can fish?

   Symbolically, the fishing area, F, is the total area, T, less the areas of A, B, and C, plus the areas of AB, AC, and BC (each of which includes ABC), minus the area ABC. The *numerical* values are left as an exercise for the reader.

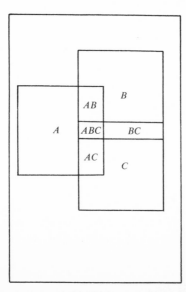

Figure 91. The fisherman's dilemma.

2. Suppose that the number n has the distinct prime factors $p_1, p_2, \ldots, p_r$, and the number of numbers from 1 to n having no prime factor in common with n are sought. This number is denoted $\phi(n)$, and is called *Euler's phi-function of n*. (For various reasons, the number 1 is *not* regarded as a prime number. If it were, every number up to n would have this factor in common with n, and $\phi(n)$ would always be 0.) Thus $\phi(1) = 1$, $\phi(2) = 1$, $\phi(3) = 2$, $\phi(4) = 2$, $\phi(5) = 4$, $\phi(6) = 2$, $\phi(7) = 6$, $\phi(8) = 4$, and so on. Let P_1 be the property of being divisible by p_1, let P_2 be the property of being divisible by p_2, and so forth. Then, applying Theorem 6,

$$\phi(n) = n - (n_1 + n_2 + \cdots + n_r) + (n_{1,2} + n_{1,3} + \cdots)$$

$$- (n_{1,2,3} + \cdots) \pm \cdots = n - \left(\frac{n}{p_1} + \frac{n}{p_2} + \cdots + \frac{n}{p_r}\right)$$

$$+ \left(\frac{n}{p_1 p_2} + \frac{n}{p_1 p_3} + \cdots + \frac{n}{p_{r-1} p_r}\right)$$

$$- \left(\frac{n}{p_1 p_2 p_3} + \frac{n}{p_1 p_2 p_4} + \cdots\right) + - \cdots \pm \frac{n}{p_1 p_2 \cdots p_r}$$

$$= n\left(1 - \frac{1}{p_1}\right)\left(1 - \frac{1}{p_2}\right) \cdots \left(1 - \frac{1}{p_r}\right).$$

EXERCISES

13. For each value of n from 1 to 15, list the numbers up to n that have no prime factors in common with n. (The prime numbers in this range are 2, 3, 5, 7, 11, 13). Compare the sizes of these lists with the formula $\phi(n) = n\left(1 - \frac{1}{p_1}\right)\left(1 - \frac{1}{p_2}\right) \cdots \left(1 - \frac{1}{p_r}\right)$ just derived.

14. Let $p_1, p_2, \ldots, p_m$ be all the prime numbers up to $\sqrt{x}$. Show that the number of prime numbers up to x, denoted $\pi(x)$, is given by

$$\pi(x) = m - 1 + [x] - \left(\left[\frac{x}{p_1}\right] + \left[\frac{x}{p_2}\right] + \cdots + \left[\frac{x}{p_m}\right]\right)$$

$$+ \left(\left[\frac{x}{p_1 p_2}\right] + \left[\frac{x}{p_1 p_3}\right] + \cdots + \left[\frac{x}{p_{m-1} p_m}\right]\right)$$

$$- \cdots \pm \left[\frac{x}{p_1 p_2 \cdots p_m}\right],$$

where $\left[\frac{x}{p}\right]$ is the integer part of $\frac{x}{p}$, that is, $\frac{x}{p}$ rounded *downward* if it is not an exact integer (an integer is any whole number). (*Hints:* (*a*) If a number between 1 and x is not prime, one of its prime factors must be less than $\sqrt{x}$. Why? (*b*) The number of multiples of p up to x is $\left\lceil \dfrac{x}{p} \right\rceil$. Why? (*c*) It must be remembered to include the *first m* primes in $\pi(x)$; and to reject 1 as a non-prime.)

15. The prime numbers up to $\sqrt{100}$ are 2, 3, 5, 7. Use the formula of the previous problem to determine $\pi(100)$. Does the answer agree with a list of the primes up to 100?

16. Among a population of 50 stray dogs, 12 had distemper, 18 had skin parasites, 11 had worms, 6 had rabies, 5 had distemper and skin parasites, 3 had skin parasites and rabies, 4 had distemper and worms, 5 had skin parasites and worms, and 2 had distemper, skin parasites, and worms. Assuming there were no other ailments or combinations thereof, how many of the dogs were healthy?

COUNTING THE DISSIMILAR CASES

To count the number of cows in a field, it suffices to add together the number of legs and divide by 4. To find the number of automobiles in a parking lot, one could count the number of wheels and divide by 4. However, if the parking lot contains bicycles and wheelbarrows as well as automobiles, then the number of vehicles is no longer $\frac{1}{4}$ the total number of wheels. In fact, the number of vehicles, V, is given by the formula

$$V = \tfrac{1}{4}(A + 2B + 4W)$$

where A is the number of automobile wheels, B is the number of bicycle wheels, and W is the number of wheelbarrow wheels. Of course, $\frac{1}{4}A$ is the number of automobiles, $\frac{1}{2}B$ is the number of bicycles, and W is the number of wheelbarrows, and the formula for V is simply the sum of these 3 terms. This expression, as will be seen, illustrates a very general counting formula, in which the individual terms may not correspond so simply to the objects being counted.

Suppose that gloves come in 3 colors: red (R), white (W), and blue (B). A left glove and a right glove are chosen at random. How many distinguishable cases are there? Since there were 3 possibilities for the *left* glove, and 3 possibilities for the *right* glove, there are $3^2 = 9$ distinguishable pairs, namely $RR, RW, RB, WR, WW, WB, BR, BW, BB$.

Suppose that instead of gloves, socks are being selected from the same 3 colors. Now there is no longer a distinction between left and right. The first impulse is to divide the previous answer by 2. However, since $\frac{9}{2}$ is not a whole number, it is clear that the approach was too naive. The dissimilar pairs can be grouped 2 at a time:

RW with WR

RB with BR

BW with WB.

However, the *matched* pairs must still be counted individually:

RR

WW

BB.

Thus, there are 6 distinguishable pairs of socks possible. A *formula* that gives the number, N, of distinguishable cases, after allowing interchange of left and right, where the original number of cases (not allowing for the symmetry) was T, is

$$N = \tfrac{1}{2}(T + C)$$

where C is the number of *symmetric* cases. In the case just considered, $T = 9$ and $C = 3$, so that $N = \frac{1}{2}(9 + 3) = 6$. More generally, if the socks came in a distinct colors, we would have $T = a^2$ and $C = a$, so that the number of distinguishable pairs of socks would be $N = \frac{1}{2}(a^2 + a) = \frac{1}{2}a(a + 1)$.

Interchanging left and right is an operation that, when repeated, returns the case to its original position. Any symmetry operation which is $\frac{1}{2}$ of a 2-step operation that returns to the starting point is called an *involution*. Some examples of involutions are: rotating a plane figure 180 degrees; turning something inside out, interchanging top and bottom; taking the reciprocal, $\frac{1}{x}$, of a nonzero number, x; and taking the negative, $-x$, of any number, x. The formula $N = \frac{1}{2}(T + C)$ gives the number of distinguishable cases for any involution, where, as before, T is the total number of cases before considering the involution, and C is the number of cases whose appearance remains unchanged, or unaffected, or, to use the terminology of higher mathematics, *invariant* under the involution.

EXERCISES

17. Two 3-digit numbers will be put in the same category if 1 of them contains the same digits as the other in reverse order. (Some numbers, like 131, will be in a category by themselves.) Into how many categories will the 1,000 numbers from 000 to 999 be placed?

18. All possible "words" consisting of any 4 English letters are formed. If words read backward are considered equivalent to words read forward, how many inequivalent 4-letter "words" are there?

19. A string of beads is formed by placing k beads on the string, where each bead is any one of n colors. If a string is "turned around," it is not possible to tell that it was not originally constructed in the reverse direction. How many *distinguishable* strings of beads are there? (*Hint:* Treat the cases where k is even and the cases where k is odd separately.) Verify the results for $n = 2$ and 3 with $k = 4$ and 5.

20. Each card in a deck of blank index cards is marked with a number on both sides. First, a number from 1 to 5 is stamped on one side. Then a number from 3 to 9 is stamped on the reverse side. How many distinguishable situations can result? There is no way to distinguish "top" from "bottom" on a blank card. (*Hint:* It is easy to list all the distinct cases to check your result.)

Figure 92. Seven distinguishable ways to clip the corners of a rectangular card.

a

b

c

21. A set of "double-6" dominoes contains every distinct pair of numbers from 00 to 66 (using the digits 0 through 6) exactly once. How many dominoes are there in a set? A set of double-9 dominoes contains every distinct pair from 00 to 99. How large is the double-9 set?

Suppose there is a deck of 3 inch × 5 inch blank index cards, and corners are to be cut out of some of the cards. (Imagine a cut corner as the removal of an isosceles right triangle whose leg is $\frac{1}{2}$ inch long.) Any number of corners, from 0 to 4, may be clipped on a single card. How many distinguishable cases of mutilated cards are there?

If the *symmetries* of the cards did not have to be considered, the problem would be relatively easy. Specifically, if front could be distinguished from back, right from left, and top from bottom on each card, the corners would be designated upper right, upper left, lower right, and lower left. Each of these 4 corners could be either notched or unnotched, so that by Theorem 1, there are $2^4 = 16$ possibilities. However, with the 4 corners indistinguishable, another approach must be used.

The "brute force" approach is to enumerate cases:

1. No corners clipped.

2. One corner clipped.

3. Two adjacent corners on short side clipped.

4. Two adjacent corners on long side clipped.

5. Two diagonally opposite corners clipped.

6. Any 3 corners clipped.

7. All 4 corners clipped.

These 7 conditions are shown in Figure 92.

e   *f*   *g*

93

A more methodical approach to the problem is to observe that *symmetries* of the index card correspond to 3 distinct *involutions:*

1. Rotating 180 degrees around the center (in the plane).
2. Rotating 180 degrees around the horizontal midline (turns card over).
3. Rotating 180 degrees around the vertical midline (turns card over).

(Strictly speaking, there is also a fourth symmetry operation, the "identity operator," which does not move the figure at all.)

Note that Figures 92*b* and 92*f* are changed by all 3 of the involutions, while 92*a* and 92*g* are not changed by any of them. Also, 92*c* is left fixed by Point 2 above, 92*d* is left fixed by Point 3, and 92*e* is left fixed by Point 1.

To count the distinguishable cases in Figure 92, one begins as before by dividing the original number of cases ($2^4 = 16$) by the number of symmetry operators (4, including the identity), but one must be careful to add in the terms for the number of cards that are symmetric under each of the involutions. The expression now becomes

$$N = \tfrac{1}{4}(T + C_a + C_b + C_c),$$

where N is the number of distinguishable cases, T is the total number of cases before allowing symmetries, C_a is the number of original cases left fixed by the Symmetry Operator 1, C_b is the number of original cases left fixed by Operator 2, and C_c is the number of original cases left fixed by Operator 3.

In the problem under consideration, $T = 16$. The cases, C_a, that are unaffected by 180 degree rotation around the center are those where the upper-right corner is the same as the lower left while the upper-left corner is the same as the lower right. There are clearly 4 such cases—the upper right–lower left pair may be either clipped or unclipped and the upper left–lower right pair may be either clipped or unclipped. Similarly, the number of cases for C_b is 4, since again there are 2 *pairs* of corners: upper right–lower right, and upper left–lower left. Finally, there are also 4 cases for C_c, where the pairing now is upper corners together and lower ones together. The formula therefore yields

$$N = \tfrac{1}{4}(16 + 4 + 4 + 4) = 7,$$

as required.

Instead of *clipping* the corners of the index cards, they could be *dipped* into different colors of paint. Suppose there are 3 colors: red, white, and blue (where "white" could be the same as "undipped"). The total number of situations before considering symmetries is now $T = 3^4 = 81$, while $C_a = C_b = C_c = 3^2 = 9$. Thus, in this case, $N = \tfrac{1}{4}(81 + 9 + 9 + 9) = 27$.

EXERCISES

22. Draw the 27 distinguishable cases involving red, white, and blue corners.

23. What is the formula for the number of distinguishable index cards when there are n possible colors for the corners?

To return briefly to the case of the vehicles in the parking lot, it will be agreed to call 2 wheels "equivalent" if they are on the same vehicle. Thus, by definition, the number of classes of equivalent wheels equals the number of vehicles. The wheelbase of an automobile is a rectangle, like an index card, and the symmetries of the index cards can be used not only for the automobiles, but also for the bicycles and the wheelbarrows, as indicated in Figure 93. In this context, $T = A + B + W$, the total number of wheels. Next, $C_a = W$, since rotating an automobile or a bicycle 180 degrees leaves none of the wheels in the same place, while the wheelbarrow wheel *does* remain fixed under these circumstances. Similarly, $C_b = W$, since again front and back wheels are being interchanged (though not in criss-cross

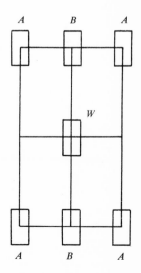

Figure 93. Wheels of an automobile (A), bicycle (B), and wheelbarrow (W).

fashion as before). Finally, $C_c = B + W$, since the right-to-left symmetry leaves bicycle wheels as well as wheelbarrow wheels fixed. Thus, as before, the number of *vehicles* is

$$N = \tfrac{1}{4}\{(A + B + W) + W + W + (B + W)\} = \tfrac{1}{4}(A + 2B + 4W).$$

EXERCISES

24. A 2×3 hexomino is to be made of 6 square tiles. Each tile can be chosen from a set of 5 colors. How many distinguishable colored hexominoes can be formed?

25. What capital letters in the English alphabet have the same set of 4 symmetries as the index card (and other rectangles)? How would you approximate these shapes as polyominoes?

26. An $a \times b$ rectangle (where a and b are unequal) is to be pasted together using black and white 1×1 squares. How many distinguishable patchwork rectangles can result? Colors are visible on both sides, and turning over is permitted. (*Hint:* Distinguish the cases where a and b are both odd, both even, and of unlike parity.)

The squares of a 2×2 checkerboard are to be colored in 1 of 2 colors. How many distinguishable cases are there if *rotations* of the checkerboard, but not *reflections* are allowed as symmetries? The 6 distinguishable cases are shown in Figure 94. The number of cases would not be reduced further by allowing reflections as symmetries, too. However, if the same problem is considered for the 3×3 checkerboard,

Figure 94. Distinguishable ways to color a 2×2 checkerboard with 2 colors.

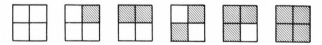

there are examples of mirror twins that are distinct if only rotations are allowed. Two such examples are shown in Figure 95.

Figure 95. Distinct mirror-image pairs.

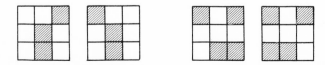

The *symmetries* of a square under rotations are 0-degree rotation (the identity), 90-degree rotation, 180-degree rotation, and 270-degree rotation (or, equivalently, -90-degree rotation). To count the number, N, of distinguishable cases under these rotations, the same sort of formula as before is used:

$$N = \tfrac{1}{4}(T + C_{90} + C_{180} + C_{270}),$$

where C_θ is the number of cases left fixed by a rotation of angle θ. Note that the total number, T, of cases *before* considering rotations is really C_0; and in general, the T in these formulas is the number of cases left fixed by the "identity operator." Also, it will always turn out that $C_{90} = C_{270}$, because if a figure looks the same after it is rotated *forward* by 90 degrees, it will certainly look the same if it is rotated backward by 90 degrees. Thus, our formula can be rewritten as

$$N = \tfrac{1}{4}(T + 2C_{90} + C_{180}).$$

For the 2×2 checkerboard in 2 colors, $T = 2^4 = 16$, since each of 4 squares can be colored either light or dark. Next, $C_{90} = 2$, since the 2×2 board will only look the same after 90 degree rotation if all squares are the same color—either all light or all dark. Finally, $C_{180} = 2^2 = 4$, since the requirement for invariance under 180-degree rotation is that opposite corners must have the same color, with 2 possible colors for each of 2 pairs of corners. The formula therefore gives

$$N = \tfrac{1}{4}(16 + 2 \cdot 2 + 4) = 6,$$

which is the number of cases shown in Figure 94.

EXERCISES

27. How many distinguishable 2×2 boards, under rotation, are there if each square may be 1 of 3 colors? Check your answer by drawing the distinguishable cases.

28. A square is cut into 4 triangular regions by its diagonals. If 3 colors are allowed for the triangular regions, how many distinguishable colorings, allowing rotation, are there? (Is this the

same as the answer to the previous problem?) Arrange a complete set of these colored squares in a rectangle, so that adjacent triangular regions of adjacent squares have the same color and the outer border is colored in a single color.

29. How many distinguishable 2×2 boards, allowing rotation and not reflection, are there if 4 colors may be used for the squares? What is the general answer if n colors are allowed? Can you show directly (algebraically) that this number is always an integer?

30. How many 3×3 boards, distinguishable under rotation, are there if 2 colors may be used for the squares? Can you draw all these cases?

31. How many distinguishable 3×3 boards are there, under rotation, if n colors may be used for the squares?

32. Derive general formulas for the number of distinguishable $k \times k$ boards, under rotation, where n colors may be used for the squares. (*Hint:* Treat odd k and even k as separate cases.)

33. Find an octomino that is symmetric under 90-degree rotation. In how many ways could 8 square tiles, each either black or white, be glued together to form this figure?

34. Beads are available in n colors. Four beads are chosen and placed on a string, and the ends of the string are tied together. How many of the resulting necklaces are distinguishable if 2 necklaces that differ only by rotation of the beads around the string are regarded as being the same?

It is now possible to consider the full set of symmetries of the square, including rotations and reflections. Consider the square in Figure 96. In addition to the 4 rotations of 0, 90,

Figure 96. The 8 symmetries of the square.

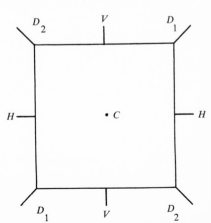

180, and 270 degrees around the center, C, there are reflections around the 4 axes: horizontal axis HH, vertical axis VV, diagonal axis D_1D_1, and diagonal axis D_2D_2. (These 8 symmetries comprise what is known as the *dihedral group of the square.*)

As a typical problem, suppose 1 monomino (or 1 checker) is to be placed on the 8×8 board. It is clear from Figure 97 that there are 10 *inequivalent* locations under rotation and reflection. However, the answer also can be *computed* by a formula for the number N of inequivalent cases under all the (dihedral) symmetries of the square. Analogous to the previous cases, the formula is

$$N = \tfrac{1}{8}(T + C_{90} + C_{180} + C_{270} + C_V + C_H + C_{D_1} + C_{D_2})$$
$$= \tfrac{1}{8}(T + 2C_{90} + C_{180} + 2C_H + 2C_D).$$

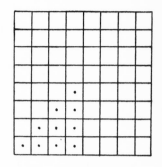

Figure 97. The 10 inequivalent locations for a monomino on the checkerboard.

Here, T is the total number of cases before symmetry considerations begin, and C_{90}, C_{180}, C_{270} are as in the previous formula. Also, C_V, C_H, C_{D_1}, and C_{D_2} are the number of configurations left invariant by reflections in the vertical, horizontal, first diagonal, and second diagonal axes, respectively. As before, $C_{90} = C_{270}$, and moreover $C_V = C_H$ and $C_{D_1} = C_{D_2}$, which leads to the second form of the formula.

For the 1-monomino problem at hand, $T = 64$, since there are initially 64 possible locations for a monomino on an 8×8 board. Next, $C_{90} = 0$, since a 90-degree rotation will surely *move* the monomino to a previously empty square. Likewise, $C_{180} = 0$, and $C_H = 0$. However, $C_D = 8$, since the monomino could be placed anywhere along a diagonal and not have its position affected by reflection in that diagonal. Thus,

$$N = \tfrac{1}{8}(T + 2C_D) = \tfrac{1}{8}(64 + 16) = 10, \text{ as required.}$$

As another example, suppose 2 monominoes are to be placed on a 4×4 board. In this case, $T = \binom{16}{2} = 120$. Again, $C_{90} = 0$; but $C_{180} = 8$, since for any location of 1 monomino in the bottom half, there is a corresponding location, rotating 180 degrees around the center, in the top half. Similarly, $C_H = 8$. Finally, $C_D = 6 + \binom{4}{2} = 12$, since there are 6 ways to place 1 monomino above the diagonal, using the other as its reflection *below* the diagonal, and $\binom{4}{2}$ ways to place both monominoes on the diagonal. This leads to the following number of inequivalent cases:

$$N = \tfrac{1}{8}(T + C_{180} + 2C_H + 2C_D) = \tfrac{1}{8}(120 + 8 + 16 + 24) = 21.$$

The 21 cases are shown in Figure 98.

EXERCISES

35. In how many inequivalent ways can 3 monominoes be placed on a 3×3 board? (Compare the formula with a drawing of all cases.)

36. In how many inequivalent ways can 4 monominoes be placed on the 4×4 board? On the 6×6 board? On the 8×8 board?

37. In how many inequivalent ways (under the dihedral symmetry group) can a 4×4 checkerboard be colored in 3 colors?

38. In how many inequivalent ways can a 3×3 tic-tac-toe board be covered with 5 X's and 4 O's.

Figure 98. The 21 inequivalent ways to place 2 monominoes on a 4 × 4 board.

39. In how many ways can 6 monominoes be placed on an 8×8 checkerboard so that every rank and every file contains an *even* number of monominoes? First determine the number, T, of solutions *without* regard to symmetries, and then determine the number N of solutions inequivalent under the rotations and reflections of the square.

40. In how many inequivalent ways can 1 monomino be placed on an $n \times n$ board? How many inequivalent ways are there for 2 monominoes? (*Hint:* It is often helpful to separate the even from the odd values of n.)

41. Classify the 12 pentominoes according to the type of symmetry groups they possess. Which one has the same symmetries as the square? Which have an involution as a symmetry? Which have only the trivial identity symmetry?

42. In how many distinguishable ways can the 5 squares of the X pentomino be colored using 3 possible colors? How many of these actually make use of all 3 of the colors?

43. In how many ways can 4 rooks be placed on a 4×4 board so that no 2 can attack one another? Solve the problem first without regard for symmetries and then determine the number of cases distinguishable under the rotations and reflections of the square.

44. Solve the preceding problem for 6 rooks on a 6×6 board and for 8 rooks on an 8×8 board.

The enumeration formulas of the previous section are all special cases of a very general formula discovered by William Burnside, the English mathematician, some 6 decades ago, and applied with great success by the Hungarian-American mathematician G. Pólya in the 1940's to problems of mathematical and scientific interest. The general formula may be stated as follows:

Theorem 7. Let S be any finite collection of objects, and let G be a finite group of *symmetries* for these objects, with n symmetry operations $g_1, g_2, \ldots, g_n$ comprising G. (One of these symmetry operations must be the identity operator.) Let $C(g)$ denote the number of objects in the collection, S, left fixed by the symmetry, g, of G. Then the number, N, of objects in S *distinguishable relative to the symmetries of G* is given by

$$N = \frac{1}{n}[C(g_1) + C(g_2) + C(g_3) + \cdots + C(g_n)].$$

(If g_1 is the identity operator of G, then $C(g_1) = T$, the total number of objects in S.)

While this formula is simple in appearance and relatively easy to apply, a rigorous proof of it would require an excursion into advanced mathematical theory. The interested reader is referred instead to the author's article on discrete classification and to John Riordan's volume, both cited in the Bibliography, for a complete proof and more extensive applications.

The reader should attempt to derive each of the 4 formulas of the previous section (for involution, rectangle group, rotation group of the square, and dihedral group of the square) from the general formula of Theorem 7.

For every regular *polygon* (a polygon is a closed plane figure bounded by straight lines), there is the group of rotations (called the *cyclic* group of the polygon, because it consists of all the rotations by multiples of $360/r$ degrees, which have the effect of cycling the polygon about its center), and the group of rotations and reflections (called the *dihedral* group of the polygon). For a regular r-gon, the cyclic group consists of r symmetries, and the dihedral group consists of $2r$ symmetries.

Solid figures also have interesting symmetry groups. For example, the group of all spatial rotations of the regular *tetrahedron* (a solid of 4 faces) is one of 12 symmetries. The rotation group of the cube, and also of the regular *octahedron* (a solid of 8 faces), is a group of 24 symmetries. Moreover, the rotation group of the regular *dodecahedron,* a solid with 12 regular pentagons as faces, and also of the regular *icosahedron,* which has 20 equilateral triangles as faces, is a group of 60 symmetries.

For the ambitious reader, the adaptation and application of the Pólya-Burnside formula of Theorem 7 to some of these new situations is developed in the following final exercises of the chapter.

EXERCISES

45. The 6 edges of a regular hexagon are each to be drawn in either black or red. How many cyclically distinct hexagons can result? (*Hint:* $N = \frac{1}{6}(C_0 + C_{60} + C_{120} + C_{180} + C_{240} + C_{300})$.) Draw all the cases.

46. In the previous problem, suppose it is also permitted to turn the hexagons over. How many distinguishable cases now exist?

47. Rework the preceding 2 problems allowing 3 colors for the edges. Then allow 4 colors. Finally, examine the problem when k colors are used.

48. The vertices of an equilateral triangle are to be colored from a set of 5 colors. If rotations and reflections of the triangle are permitted, how many distinct cases can result?

49. Let p be any prime number except 2 (thus, $p = 3, 5, 7, 11, 13, 17, \ldots$). Beads are available in b colors, and p beads are put on a string. How many distinct strings can be formed? The ends of the string are tied together to form a necklace. Under cyclic rotations, how many distinct necklaces are there? If it is also

allowed to turn the necklaces over, how many distinguishable cases are there? Verify your result for $b = 2$ colors, and $p = 5$ beads on a string; also for $b = 4, p = 3$.

50. Identify the 24 rotational symmetries of a cube. (*Hint:* There are 3 kinds of *axes* going through the center of a cube—face-to-face, edge-to-edge, and vertex-to-vertex. Examine the kinds of rotations around each such axis.)

51. Six distinct colors of paint are available, and the 6 faces of a cube are to be painted, each with a different color. Show that this can be done in 30 essentially distinct ways.

52. How many distinct cubes are there with 3 black faces and 3 white faces?

53. How many distinct cubes are there with 2 red, 2 white, and 2 blue faces?

54. In how many essentially different ways can the 8 *vertices* of a cube each be either labeled or unlabeled? How many of these cases involve 4 labeled vertices and 4 unlabeled vertices? Draw all of these 4-and-4 cases.

CHAPTER VI

Bigger Polyominoes and Higher Dimensions

THE mathematical theory of enumeration and certain notions of symmetry, including rotations and reflections, were developed in some detail in the last chapter. Some of these ideas will now be applied to the further study of polyominoes and to their extensions in more than 2 dimensions.

ONE-SIDED POLYOMINOES

Up to this point it has been assumed that polyominoes can be both rotated and reflected, or flopped over, at will. However, if they are confined strictly to the plane, the figures can still be rotated, but cannot be reflected. Polyominoes that cannot be turned over may be termed one-sided, and, in general, eliminating reflection increases the number of *n*-ominoes. Thus, although there are still only 1 monomino, 1 domino, and 2 trominoes, 7 tetrominoes are now distinguished (instead of 5), 18 pentominoes (instead of 12), 60 hexominoes (instead of 35), and so on. As with the 5 two-sided tetrominoes, the 7 one-sided tetrominoes cannot be arranged in any rectangle, but are shown in a connected pattern in Figure 99. The 18 one-sided pentominoes are arranged in a 9 × 10 rectangle in Figure 100. (The percentage of one-sided *n*-ominoes that are distinct from their mirror images increases toward 100 per cent as *n* increases.) Now, although the possibility of considering one-sided polyominoes has been pointed out, attention will again be focused on the two-sided case; but it should be remembered that this distinction can always be made.

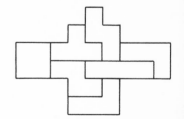

Figure 99. An almost symmetric pattern with the one-sided tetrominoes.

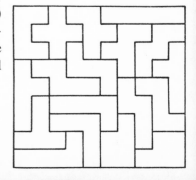

Figure 100. The 18 one-sided pentominoes arranged in a rectangle.

POLYOMINOES

There are 35 distinct hexominoes, which cover an aggregate area of 210 squares. Rather surprisingly, however, they will not fit together into any *rectangle,* whether 3×70, or 5×42, or 6×35, or 7×30, or 10×21, or 14×15. (This was proved at the end of Chapter I by a simple argument involving checkerboard coloring.) However, as shown some years ago in the British publication, no longer issued, called *Fairy Chess Review,* other interesting arrangements of the 35 hexominoes are possible. Two of these are shown in Figures 101 and 102.

There are 108 heptominoes, including one with a hole (shaded in Figure 103). However, since this figure cannot be made to "fit" with other heptominoes except in patterns with "holes," one may sometimes prefer to exclude it from the approved list. The remaining heptominoes cover a total area of $7 \times 107 = 749$ squares. The only rectangle they can possibly occupy is a 7×107 one. A particularly interesting solution to fitting the 107 heptominoes together, consisting of one 7×7 square and four 7×25 rectangles, was found

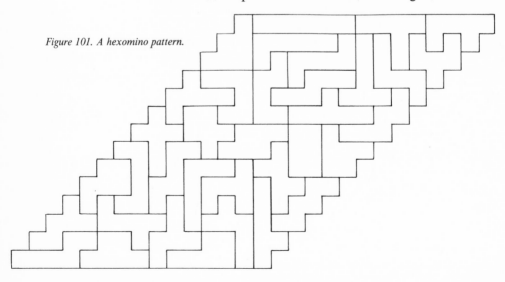

Figure 101. A hexomino pattern.

Figure 102. A symmetrical hex-omino pattern.

by David A. Klarner, while a student at Humboldt State College in California, and is shown in Figure 104. The reader is invited to look for other solutions to this type of construction. Another problem, also first solved by Klarner, is to arrange all 108 heptominoes into three 11 × 23 rectangles, each with the center square removed. Klarner's solution to this one appears in Figure 103.

THE HIGHER n-OMINOES

The following table is the best now available for the number of *n*-ominoes as a function of *n*. No reliable compilation of the number of *n*-ominoes has been reported for values of *n* greater than 10.

						n				
	1	2	3	4	5	6	7	8	9	10
Number of simply connected *n*-ominoes	1	1	2	5	12	35	107	363	1248	4271
Number of multiply connected *n*-ominoes	0	0	0	0	0	0	1	6	37	195

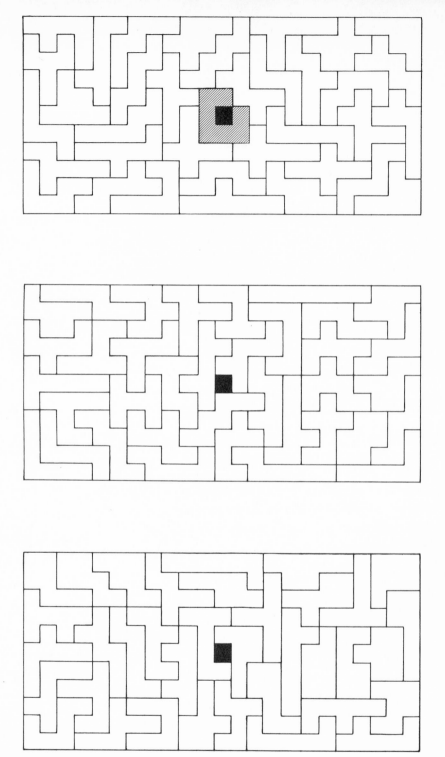

Figure 103. Three congruent rectangles made with 108 heptominoes.

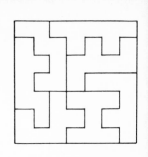

Figure 104. Four rectangles and a square with 107 heptominoes.

A multiply connected n-omino is one that has 1 or more holes in it. For example, an octomino that consists of the 8 squares surrounding an empty square is multiply connected.

The values for 9 and 10 come from a recent article in the *Canadian Journal of Mathematics* by R. C. Read, Professor of Mathematics at the University of the West Indies, Kingston, Jamaica. In the article, "Contributions to the Cell Growth Problem," methods are developed for finding the number of n-ominoes that fit inside rectangles of $1 \times p$, $2 \times p$, $3 \times p$, where p is any positive integer. Thus the final enumeration of 1285 *nonominoes* (9 squares) and 4466 *dekominoes* (10 squares) are the results of the tabulations shown below. Read's enumeration counts simply connected and multiply connected n-ominoes together, so that $1285 = 1248 + 37$ and $4466 = 4271 + 195$, as noted in the previous table.

Nonominoes		Dekominoes	
Size of Rectangle	*Number*	*Size of Rectangle*	*Number*
1×9	1	1×10	1
2×8	7	2×9	9
2×7	28	2×8	40
2×6	22	2×7	52
2×5	3	2×6	15
3×7	49	2×5	1
3×6	188	3×8	63
3×5	210	3×7	332
3×4	42	3×6	550
3×3	1	3×5	255
4×6	97	3×4	21
4×5	383	4×7	155
4×4	181	4×6	822
5×5	73	4×5	1,304
TOTAL	1285	4×4	266
		5×6	240
		5×5	340
		TOTAL	4466

An independent enumeration by the mathematician Thomas R. Parkin of the Aerospace Corporation, El Segundo, California, agrees with Read's published values except for the number of dekominoes in the 5 × 5 square, where Parkin counts 529 instead of Read's 340. An impartial audit of this discrepancy has not yet been made.

Quite unrelated to Read's enumerative techniques is a systematic method for obtaining all the $(n + 1)$-ominoes from the n-ominoes. As the method is described, it will be illustrated by the case $n = 4$. First, all the n-ominoes are arranged according to the length of the longest straight row of squares they contain. For the tetrominoes, Column I of Figure 105 is obtained.

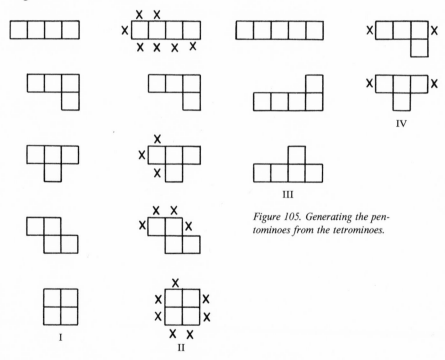

Figure 105. Generating the pentominoes from the tetrominoes.

If an n-omino possesses symmetries, its edges are closed off with x's, with the exception of 1 "typical region," as in Column II. Beginning with the longest n-omino, an extra

111

square may be attached to any *open* edge to obtain an
$(n + 1)$-omino as in Column III, while the next-longest
n-ominoes are prevented from being made as long as the
longest as in Column IV. The first of those in Column IV
may now have a square added to any open edge as shown in
Figure 106. The *n*-omino just extended must now be prevented from occurring in the possible extensions of the other
n-ominoes of the same length (see Figure 107*a*).

*Figure 106. Pentominoes generated
from the first entry of Column IV
of Figure 105.*

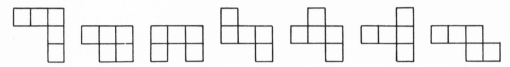

The next *n*-omino of the second-longest class is then
extended in all remaining possible ways, as in Figure 107*b*.
After all the second-longest *n*-ominoes have been extended,
the third-longest *n*-ominoes are prevented from being
extended to the length of the second-longest ones (see Figures 107*c* and 107*d*), and the procedure is repeated, yielding
Figure 107*e*.

*Figure 107. The last 2 pentominoes
are found.*

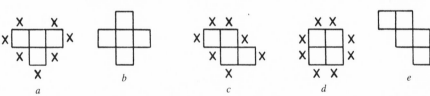

Proceeding in this fashion, all the $(n + 1)$-ominoes are
obtained from the *n*-ominoes, each exactly once. (All 12 pentominoes, in fact, have now been obtained.) This method,
while moderately lengthy, is another that is well suited to the
way in which a computer is programmed—it is both deter-
ministic and iterative. However, it is important to mention
that there is one more rule required, in general, to make the
transition from *n*-ominoes to $(n + 1)$-ominoes, for certain
values of *n*, in order to guarantee the uniqueness of the
$(n + 1)$-ominoes produced. For example, when $n = 5$, the P

pentomino does not have any symmetries, and, if taken first in the class of length-3 pentominoes, would be restricted only as shown at the left of Figure 108. If this figure is then extended, the 7 hexominoes of Figure 108 result. But c and f are the same, and it would certainly be awkward to count the same pentomino twice in the attempt at enumeration. The

Figure 108. Hexominoes generated from the P pentomino.

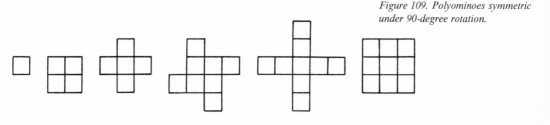

X

X   P pentomino a b c e f g

                                                            d

duplication is due to the symmetry of 90-degree rotation in the following way. First, consider the polyominoes that are symmetric under 90-degree rotation, as shown in Figure 109. An n-omino exceeding any of these figures either by 1 monomino, or by 2 monominoes 90 degrees apart, is capable of causing the same difficulty as encountered with the P pentomino. However, if the figure obtained from the 90-degree

Figure 109. Polyominoes symmetric under 90-degree rotation.

symmetric figure is itself symmetric (necessarily a reflectional symmetry) it does no actual harm. (That is, it contributes no duplicate to the enumeration.) From the symmetric polyominoes just shown in Figure 109, the shapes exceeding them by 1 monomino and by 2 monominoes 90 degrees apart are as illustrated in Figure 110. Of these, only the totally nonsymmetric ones (shaded in the figure) require special attention.   113

POLYOMINOES

Figure 110. Higher-order polyominoes derived from Figure 109.

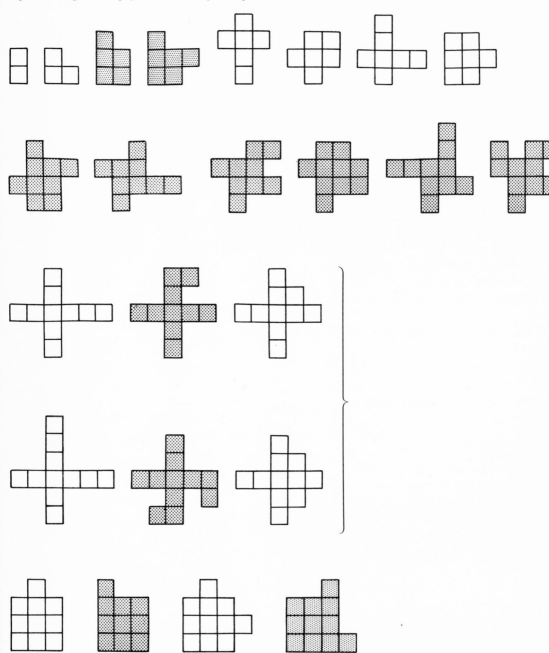

Compared to the literally thousands of polyominoes for $n < 13$ (that is, *n less than* 13), these 12 special cases are rare exceptions indeed. In a computer program or other exhaustive search, the extra $(n + 1)$-ominoes resulting from these cases could be left in the list of figures produced until the very end and then removed from the final compilation by the programmer.

The official count of the octominoes lists 369, including the 6 multiply connected cases of "doubtful" legitimacy shown in Figure 111 where the shaded region indicates a hole. These are all extensions of the multiply connected heptomino shaded in Figure 103.

Figure 111. Multiply connected octominoes.

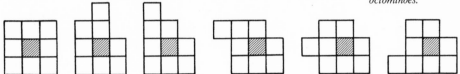

An exact expression for the number of *n*-ominoes, $P(n)$, in terms of n has not yet been found. As an empirical technique, a sequence C_n may be defined by

$$\frac{P(n + 1)}{nP(n)} = C_n.$$

and the sequence of values: $C_1 = 1$, $C_2 = 1$, $C_3 = .833$, $C_4 = .600$, $C_5 = .583$, $C_6 = .514$, $C_7 = .488$, $C_8 = .435$, $C_9 = .386$ may well converge to some limiting value. This would suggest an approximate expression of the sort

$$P(n) \approx k \cdot C^n \cdot n!,$$

where $C = \lim_{n \to \infty} C_n$. (That is, C is the limiting value of C_n as n tends toward infinity, ∞.)

115

In any case, it is easy to prove that

$$P(n + 1) < (2n + 1)P(n)$$

from the simple observation that there are at most $2n + 1$ places where an extra square can be attached to an n-omino, except for the straight n-omino. But, after allowing for symmetry, the straight n-omino can contribute at most $\dfrac{n + 3}{2}$, which is certainly less than $2n + 1$, to the list of $(n + 1)$-ominoes. This leads to the inequality $P(n) < \dfrac{(2n)!}{2^n n!}$, where $\dfrac{(2n)!}{2^n n!}$ grows like $\dfrac{1}{\sqrt{\pi n}} \, 2^n n!$, which gives an upper bound on the size of $P(n)$ that has a reasonably simple expression. This is certainly not the tightest possible result, but suggests a promising line of attack for the problem.

SOLID POLYOMINOES

Numerous pentomino fans have suggested the possibility of gluing the 12 pentominoes together using 5 cubes instead of 5 squares each, and making solid patterns from them. More generally, one can list and enumerate the solid polyominoes of every number of sides. The solid polyominoes, allowing the pieces to be reflected and rotated, up through the tetrominoes are shown in Figure 112.

Note that the first *nonplanar* figures (that is, those in which all the cubes do not lie in one plane) occur among the tetrominoes, since any 3 points lie in a plane, whereas 4 points (the centers of the 4 cubes) need not. Two of the 3 nonplanar tetrominoes are mirror twins, differing from each other as a right shoe differs from a left one.

A game invented by the contemporary Danish puzzle expert and game innovator Piet Hein and available commercially as the "Soma Cube" puzzle involves the 7 solid polyominoes that are not simple rectangular solids (6 tetrominoes and 1 tromino) shaded in Figure 112. The object is to assemble these either into a $3 \times 3 \times 3$ cube, or into any of many other intriguing shapes. (A lengthy account of these

116

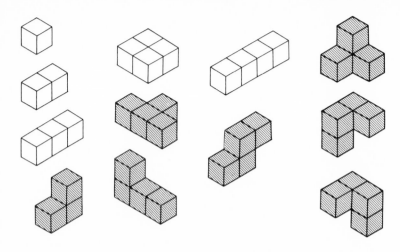

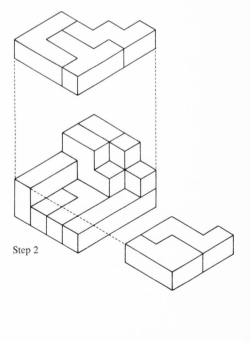

Figure 112. The lower-order solid polyominoes, with the Soma Cubes shaded.

problems is contained in the "Mathematical Games" column of *Scientific American* for September, 1958.)

If one uses the 12 planar pentominoes in their solid form, a natural problem is to fit them into a 3 × 4 × 5 rectangular solid. One of the many solutions to this problem is shown with its step by step construction in Figure 113.

Figure 113. Construction of a 3 × 4 × 5 solid using the 12 solid pentominoes.

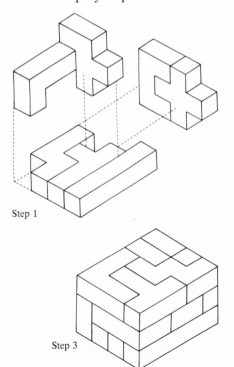

Step 1

Step 2

Step 3

In addition to the $3 \times 4 \times 5$ rectangular solid, the $2 \times 3 \times 10$ and the $2 \times 5 \times 6$ rectangular solids can also be constructed. In fact, the first "superposition problem" in Chapter II, which asks for two 5×6 rectangles using all 12 pentominoes, is a special case of the $2 \times 5 \times 6$ rectangular-solid problem.

David A. Klarner has gone even farther, producing all 29 solid pentominoes (or "pentacubes," as Klarner calls them) that are distinct under physical 3-dimensional rotations. (Thus, such mirror twins as those shown in Figure 114 count as 2 separate pieces, since neither can be rotated into the other within the confines of 3-dimensional space.) Unfortunately, since 29 is a prime, the number of simple solids using all of the solid pentominoes is rather limited. However, Klarner found that if the $1 \times 1 \times 5$ piece is omitted, the remaining 28 pentacubes can be fitted together into 2 separate $2 \times 5 \times 7$ rectangular solids. Klarner's solution is shown in Figure 115 (a dot or cross represents whether a cube extends upward or downward, respectively). Another solution, discovered by the author, is shown in Figure 116. It embodies the additional constraint that the 11 planar pieces (the $1 \times 1 \times 5$ pentomino having been discarded) all lie in the same $2 \times 5 \times 7$ rectangular solid.

The reader is invited to look for additional simple solids into which the solid pentominoes will fit and, what is even more important, to discover other interesting shapes into which they can be assembled.

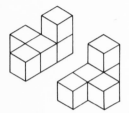

Figure 114. Mirror-twin solid pentominoes.

Figure 115. Two $2 \times 5 \times 7$ solids built with solid pentominoes.

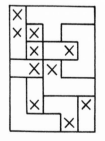
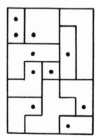
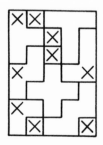
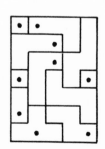

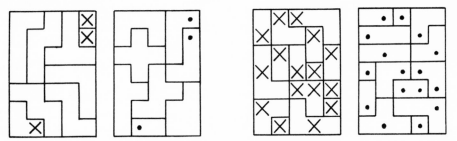

Figure 116. The two $2 \times 5 \times 7$ solids built with the planar solid pentominoes in one half.

HIGHER DIMENSIONS AND
RECTANGULAR TREES

It is not as difficult as one might imagine to list all the *n*-ominoes that can be formed in an *unlimited* number of dimensions, at least for small values of *n*; *n* connected cells never require more than $n - 1$ dimensions for their positioning, so that the pentominoes are the first case that go beyond 3 dimensions. Moreover, the construction of all *n*-ominoes requiring the full $n - 1$ dimensions is remarkably simple. When no limitation is imposed on the number of dimensions available, it is no longer reasonable to consider mirror twins as distinct; they can be rotated into coincidence in a space of higher dimension just as some of the one-sided pentominoes are distinct *in* the plane but can be flipped over into exact superposition if use is made of the third dimension.

For purposes of representation, it is convenient to replace each unit (a square, cube, or hypercube) by a single point, namely the point at its center, and to join these center points by lines if their corresponding cells are connected. Thus the tetromino of Figure 117*a* is replaced by the "tree" of Figure 117*b*. In mathematical terminology, the tree is the *projective dual* of the polyomino.

To represent a large number of dimensions, it is further convenient to introduce a scheme in which connections in

Figure 117. "Tree" representation of a tetromino.

a   *b*

119

each dimension correspond to a different type of line (solid, dotted, dashed, and so on). Figure 118 shows all the distinct monominoes, dominoes, trominoes, tetrominoes, and pentominoes of unrestricted dimension, with the first dimension (horizontal) represented by the solid line, the second dimension (vertical) by a dashed line, the third dimension by a dotted line, and the fourth dimension by a line of alternating dashes and dots.

There are only 7 tetrominoes in Figure 118, rather than 8 as in Figure 112, because the last 2 tetrominoes of Figure 112 are mirror images. Similarly, there are only 23 pentominoes of 1, 2, and 3 dimensions in Figure 118 instead of the 29 pieces identified by Klarner, because his pieces, used in Figures 115 and 116, include 6 sets of mirror twins. The last 3 pentominoes in Figure 118 are 4-dimensional.

Figure 118. Monominoes through pentominoes of unrestricted dimension.

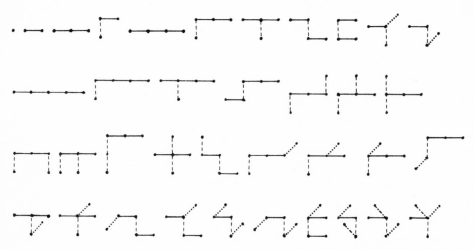

There is an extensive mathematical literature on the enumeration of dimensional trees, which is effectively summarized in Chapter 6 of John Riordan's book mentioned earlier. It is quite likely that the enumeration of "rectangular trees" of the type shown in Figure 118 could be carried out by existing methods, where rectangular trees would be defined as *trees* (a set of points simply connected by lines) with the connecting lines variously "colored." The ordinary, or uncolored, trees are shown in Figure 119, up through "order 6" (6 points and 5 connecting lines).

In attempting to establish an equivalence between polyominoes and rectangular, colored trees, the following set of rules concerning the coloring must be observed:

1. At most, 2 lines of the same color may emanate from any single point.

2. Trees that differ only by a permutation (relabeling) of the colors are considered identical.

3. Every line segment must be assigned an "orientation" (that is, *plus* or *minus*), and trees of the same color but with different line-segment orientations are only equivalent if the orientations can be made to agree by reversing the sign of *all* segments having certain colors. (The orientations are conveniently represented by arrowheads on the line segments.)

4. In any linear sequence of line segments in a tree, it is not allowed to have the same number of plus-and-minus-oriented segments of each of the colors in the sequence. (The purpose of this rule is to prevent the tree from "closing back on itself" when interpreted as a polyomino.)

Figure 119. Ordinary trees through order 6.

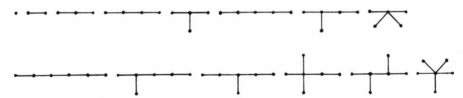

With this set of rules, the basic trees of Figure 119 become the rectangular trees of Figure 118, as shown for the monominoes, dominoes, trominoes, and tetrominoes in Figure 120.

Unfortunately, beyond this point the classification is no longer identical for polyominoes and for rectangular trees. The difficulty already encountered with certain pentominoes is illustrated by the 4 inequivalent trees in Figure 121. As indicated, each of them "folds up" into the P pentomino.

121

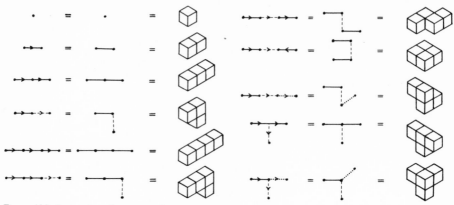

Figure 120. Conversion of trees to polyominoes.

Figure 121. Four inequivalent trees that fold up into the same P pentomino.

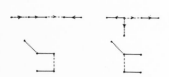

Figure 122. Two different tree representations of the same solid pentomino.

A similar illustration, involving the 2 distinct tree representations of the same solid pentomino, is shown in Figure 122. Actually, these are the only cases of multiple-tree representation for the pentominoes. However, the situation gets progressively more complicated as the size of the n-ominoes increases. It may still be possible, despite these difficulties, to apply the enumeration techniques for trees to the problem of the number of solid n-ominoes that can be derived. The restriction to *plane* polyominoes merely restricts the trees to the bichromatic (two-colored) case.

One important case in which the colored trees are a completely faithful representation of the corresponding polyominoes is the study of the number of n-ominoes that require the maximum number, namely $n - 1$, dimensions. In this

122

case, each of the $n - 1$ edges of a tree with n points (or, as they are also known, *nodes*) must be colored a different color. This effectively eliminates all questions of symmetry and orientation. Thus, there is exactly 1 such n-omino for each ordinary or unrestricted tree with n nodes; and there are no other such n-ominoes. Hence, referring back to Figure 119, there is one 1-dimensional domino, one 2-dimensional tromino, two 3-dimensional tetrominoes, three 4-dimensional pentominoes, and six 5-dimensional hexominoes. These are summarized in Figure 123, where a heavy line has been introduced as the fifth color.

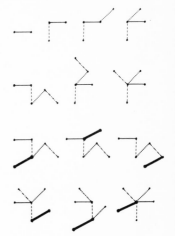

Figure 123. The n-*ominoes that require* n − 1 *dimensions.*

CHAPTER VII

Generalizations of Polyominoes

ATTENTION will now be turned to *generalizations* of polyominoes, obtained first by relaxing the connectivity requirements and then by changing the basic building blocks from squares to such shapes as triangles and hexagons. Finally, an enumeration of the number of different ways in which a $2 \times n$ rectangle can be filled with dominoes will be made.

PSEUDO- AND QUASI-POLYOMINOES

One way to generalize the notion of polyominoes is to relax the requirements by which squares must be connected. As mentioned in Chapter I, polyominoes may be regarded as being "rook-wise" connected. One can define pseudo-polyominoes as king-wise connected sets of squares; that is, the king, which can move diagonally as well as along rank and file, must be able to reach any other square of the polyomino in a finite number of moves. Even more general is the concept of quasi-polyominoes, where a quasi-n-omino is any set of n squares from a square planar array, irrespective of connectivity. These concepts were first introduced by the author in "Checkerboards and Polyominoes" in the *American Mathematical Monthly* in 1954.

The pseudo-n-ominoes for $n = 1, 2, 3$, and 4 are shown in Figure 124. The fact that the 5 pseudo-trominoes can be fitted together into a 3×5 rectangle is illustrated in Figure 125a. The only rectangles capable of including all 22 of the pseudo-tetrominoes illustrated in Figure 124 are the 8×11 and 4×22 rectangles. A simultaneous solution to both problems is obtained by constructing two 4×11 rectangles, as shown in Figure 125b.

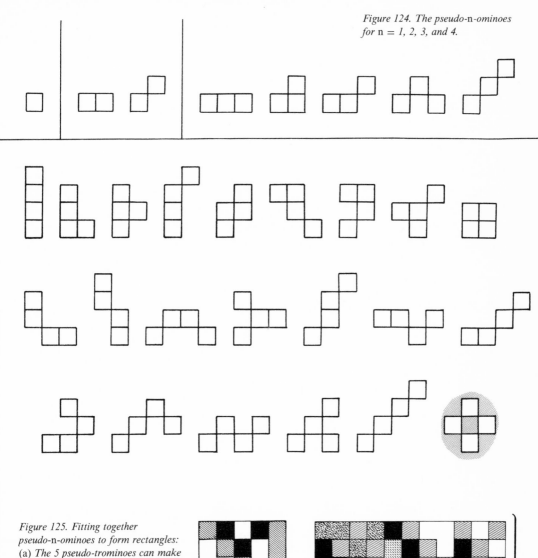

*Figure 124. The pseudo-*n-*ominoes for* n = *1, 2, 3, and 4.*

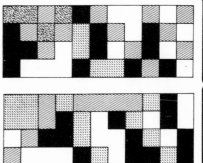

*Figure 125. Fitting together pseudo-*n-*ominoes to form rectangles:* (a) *The 5 pseudo-trominoes can make a 3 × 5 rectangle;* (b) *2 congruent rectangles constructed with the 22 pseudo-tetrominoes.*

a

b

Obviously, pseudo-polyominoes can be extended to more than 2 dimensions. Note that in 3 dimensions, there are 3 solid pseudo-dominoes and 14 solid pseudo-trominoes (not including mirror images) as shown in Figure 126. Unlike ordinary polyominoes, the number of pseudo-*n*-ominoes increases without limit as the dimension increases, even for small values of *n*. The number of pseudo-dominoes in *D* dimensions is exactly *D* (hence the 2 pseudo-dominoes in Figure 124 and the 3 in Figure 126). The number of pseudo-trominoes in *D* dimensions has not been studied, but the formula $1 + 4 + 9 + \cdots + D^2$ fits the first 3 cases, at least.

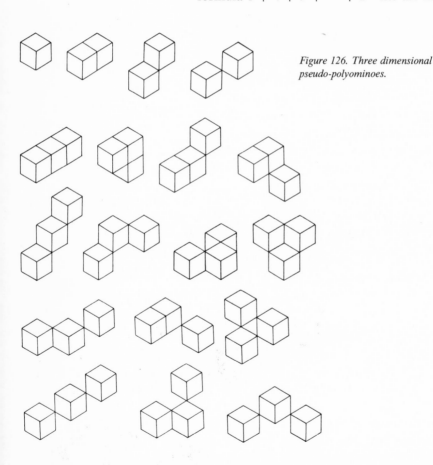

Figure 126. Three dimensional pseudo-polyominoes.

The method given earlier for obtaining all the ordinary $(n + 1)$-ominoes from the n-ominoes works equally well for pseudo-dominoes and, with any reasonable constraints on the dimensionality of the acceptable pieces, both for polyominoes and pseudo-polyominoes. In fact, precisely this method was used in arriving at Figure 124 and Figure 126. The method also applies to the trees of Chapter VI, with and without colors and constraints.

The subject of quasi-polyominoes introduces some essentially new features. For one thing, it is no longer possible to draw all "simple" cases; for example, the number of quasi-dominoes in 1 dimension is already infinite. As a result, problems of *existence* and *constructability* are more typical than the more straightforward construction and enumeration problems encountered up to this point.

A construction problem involving quasi-trominoes was given in the article "Checkerboards and Polyominoes," referred to at the beginning of this chapter. It asked for a covering of the 8×8 checkerboard using 21 of the quasi-trominoes of Figure 127a and 1 monomino. A solution is shown in Figure 127c, making use of the hexomino indicated in Figure 127b, which is assembled from 2 of the quasi-trominoes.

Figure 127. Covering a checkerboard with quasi-trominoes and a monomino.

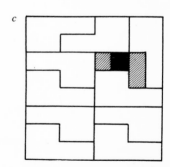

Dr. Basil Gordon, Professor of Mathematics at the University of California, Los Angeles, has been investigating quasi-polyominoes in the following context: What is the quasi-polyomino of fewest cells, in D dimensions, that *cannot* be used to fill up all of D-dimensional space?

Gordon has solved this problem for $D = 1$, where the "space" is the infinite line with uniform segments represented in Figure 128. The only quasi-monomino is the single segment (Figure 129*a*), and clearly this can be used repeatedly to fill up the "space" of Figure 128. Every quasi-domino along the segmented line can be thought of in the form shown in Figure 129*b*, where 2 unit segments are separated by an integral distance, t, for any $t = 0, 1, 2, 3, 4, \ldots$

Figure 128. Uniform segments on the infinite line.

It is clear that $t + 1$ of these quasi-dominoes can be juxtaposed to cover a solid stretch of length $2t + 2$, as indicated in Figure 129*c*, where the same number (from 0 to t) identifies a component of the same quasi-domino. It is then a trivial matter to cover the entire "space" of Figure 128 with an unlimited number of these solid stretches of length $2t + 2$.

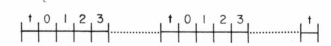

a   *b*

Figure 129. Covering the infinite line with quasi-dominoes.

c

Figure 130. The infinite line cannot be covered with this building block, without rotation.

128

For the case of quasi-trominoes, if the piece cannot be rotated, then the shape of Figure 130 is an inadequate building block, since the gap it contains can never be filled. In the more interesting case where rotation *is* permitted, Gordon has proved the remarkable theorem that *every* quasi-tromino can be used to cover the 1-dimensional space of Figure 128. For example, 2 quasi-trominoes of the type shown in Figure 130 can be interlocked "back-to-back" to form a solid segment of length 6, which can be repeated to cover the infinite line. However, Figure 131 shows a quasi-tetromino that clearly cannot succeed in covering the line. Thus, Gordon's result in 1 dimension is that every quasi-tromino, but *not* every quasi-tetromino, can be used to cover the infinite line.

Figure 131. A quasi-tetromino that cannot be used to cover the infinite line.

Considering 2 or more dimensions, Gordon has exhibited a quasi-polyomino of $3D$ cells (where D is the dimension) that cannot be used to cover, or "tile," the space. The idea is illustrated in Figure 132, where the examples for $D = 2$ and $D = 3$ are shown. (Actually, this family of examples turns out to be one of *pseudo*-polyominoes.) These examples are obtained by taking all 2-dimensional rook neighbors (rook-wise adjacent) of an empty cell, plus D additional king neighbors (king-wise adjacent), which are rook neighbors to the original rook neighbors, 2 at a time. The empty central cell is thereby isolated. (Note that this construction does not work in 1 dimension.) Although it is thus proved that there exist quasi-polyominoes of $3D$ cells that will not tile D-dimensional space (for D greater than 1), it is certainly not proved that every quasi-polyomino of $3D - 1$ or fewer cells will tile the space. In fact, it is difficult to show more than that all quasi-polyominoes of $D + 1$ cells will tile D-dimensional space.

Figure 132. Quasi-polyominoes that cannot cover the infinite space.

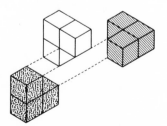

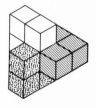

The mathematical logician Dr. E. F. Moore of the Bell Telephone Laboratories once considered a variety of problems involving the covering or tiling of D-dimensional space using an unlimited number of replicas of a finite set of "standard parts." He has formulated a challenging and profound conjecture concerning all such problems, including the quasi-polyomino covering problems just discussed. Moore's conjecture was that whenever a finite set of standard parts has the property that an unlimited number of replicas of these parts can be used to cover D-dimensional space, there is some *finite pattern* that they can cover, which can then be repeated periodically to finish covering D-dimensional space. A supporting instance of this conjecture was given in Figure 129, where the arbitrary quasi-domino was first used to fill up a solid segment, and this solid segment was then repeated periodically to cover the infinite line. Moore's conjecture did not assert that every infinite covering (one that covers the entire plane) is in fact a periodic covering (a covering of the entire plane by periodic repetition of a basic pattern). Such an assertion would be quite false. The conjecture does assert that if an infinite covering exists, then a periodic covering also exists. This conjecture appears to be exceedingly difficult to prove or disprove, and Moore even advanced the suggestion that it may be logically undecidable. Recently, however, a counter example was found by Moore and Hao Wang, Professor of Logic, Harvard University, demonstrating that certain sets of shapes can fill the plane, although they cannot fill it periodically.

The reader is invited to test the 12 ordinary, familiar pentominoes to see which of them can be used, repeating only the one shape chosen, to tile the plane. A distinction can be made between those that tile *without* allowing rotation, and those that can tile the plane only if rotated positions are allowed. An example of the latter case is shown in Figure 133.

TRIANGULAR AND HEXAGONAL ANIMALS

In his writings on polyominoes, Dr. Frank Harary, Professor of Mathematics at the University of Michigan, has

130

Figure 133. Tiling the plane with the T pentomino.

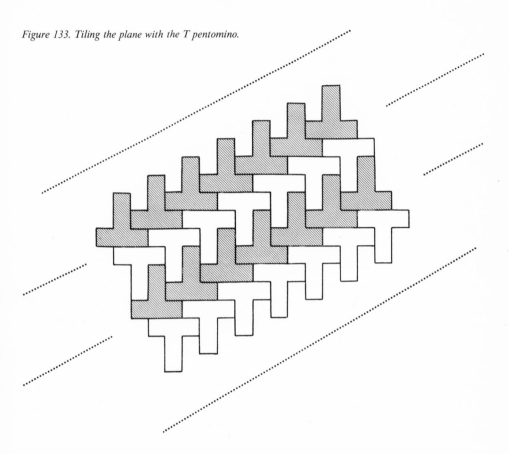

referred to *n*-ominoes as "*n*-celled animals." In his *American Mathematical Monthly* article, "Checkerboards and Polyominoes," the author suggested that other regular tilings (either triangular or hexagonal) could be used for the board and for the objects covering it. Connected combinations of equilateral triangles can be called *triangular animals* and, similarly, connected hexagons called *hexagonal animals*. The triangular animals of size *n* for *n* = 1, 2, 3, 4, and 5 are shown in Figure 134.

131

Figure 134. *Triangular animals of size* n *up through* n = 5.

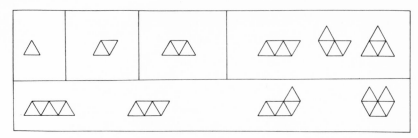

Figure 135. A rhombus covered
with the 12 triangular animals of
size 6.

In a recent article, "Maestro puzzles" (the name under which the pentomino puzzle is marketed commercially in England), in the *Mathematical Gazette,* the English mathematicians J. E. Reeve and J. A. Tyrrell consider patterns that can be formed using all 12 triangular animals 6 triangles in size. They report having discovered more than 40 solutions to the covering of the rhombus shown in Figure 135, which exhibits one of these solutions.

Reeve and Tyrrell also consider the problem of arranging 9 of these 12 triangular animals into the regular hexagon of Figure 136. They point out that there are $\binom{12}{9} = 220$ ways to decide which 9 of the 12 to use, and that 90 of these 220 possible solutions are clearly impossible because they involve using one but not both of the 2 "unbalanced" animals of Figure 137. Since the entire hexagon of Figure 136 is "balanced" in alternating colors, it is clear that it cannot be covered if an odd number of the unbalanced animals are used. Reeve and Tyrrell assert in their article that 22 of the remaining 130 problems are insoluble, "but [they] have been unable

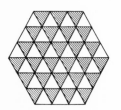

Figure 136. A regular hexagon.

Figure 137. The balanced and
unbalanced hexagonal animals.

Balanced Animals   Unbalanced Animals

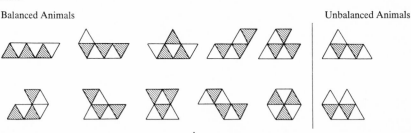

to find a simple proof of this." The reader is encouraged to try his hand at these problems, and to investigate other interesting patterns into which triangular animals may or may not fit. For example, can the 7 animals of 4 and 5 triangles be fitted into the rhombus shown in Figure 138?

In his column "Puzzles and Paradoxes" in the British periodical *New Scientist*, T. H. O'Beirne has devoted considerable space to problems involving the triangular animals. Calling 2 equilateral triangles joined to form a rhombus a *diamond,* he generalizes this to triamonds, tetriamonds, pentiamonds, hexiamonds, and so on. He has named the 12 *hexiamonds* (6 connected triangles) as shown in Figure 139. Many of O'Beirne's constructions involve the

Figure 138. A rhombus.

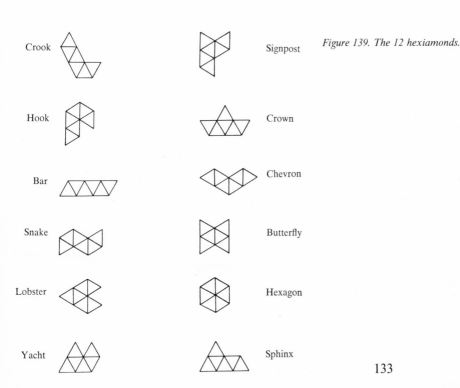

Figure 139. The 12 hexiamonds.

Crook

Hook

Bar

Snake

Lobster

Yacht

Signpost

Crown

Chevron

Butterfly

Hexagon

Sphinx

133

Figure 140. A honeycomb to be filled with the 19 one-sided hexiamonds.

use of 19 hexiamonds—the mirror images of the 7 asymmetric hexiamonds are added to the 12 shapes already considered. One problem is to fit these 19 pieces into 3 hexagons, 1 being the hexagonal piece itself, and each of the other 2 being the hexagon shown in Figure 136. Also discussed at length are problems of filling up the honeycomb shape of Figure 140.

There are 24 *heptiamonds* (7 connected triangles), as shown in Figure 141. The reader is encouraged to look for interesting configurations that this set of shapes will cover.

Figure 141. The 24 heptiamonds.

If a dot is placed at the center of each cell in the square tiling of the plane, the vertices of a similar square tiling appear. However, if this is done to triangular tiling, the vertices of hexagonal tiling appear, and the dots in the center of hexagonal tiling indicate vertices of triangular tiling. The triangular and hexagonal tilings are therefore dual configurations, whereas the square tiling is self-dual. As shown in

Figure 136, the triangular tiling admits a checkerboard coloring. This is not possible with hexagonal coverage. However, there is a three-color analog of the checkerboard coloring for hexagonal tiling, as illustrated in Figure 142.

The simplest hexagonal animals have been studied by chemists—although not under that name—as models of the molecular structure of organic compounds. Hexagonal animals of 1, 2, 3, 4, and 5 hexagons are shown in Figure 143. There has been no previously published problem literature on this subject, so the reader is invited to explore virgin territory and propose interesting configurations for the hexagonal animals.

Figure 142. Three-color hexagonal tiling.

RECTANGLES OF DOMINOES

Another type of polyomino problem is to derive mathematical expressions for the number of ways that a given set of polyominoes can fill up a specified region. Obviously, this is extremely difficult to do in general, but a special case in which the answer is rather easy to obtain and is quite elegant will now be presented.

In the Problem Section of the May, 1961, issue of *American Mathematical Monthly,* Mr. W. E. Patton proposed the following problem: "It is desired to form a 2 × n rectangle from 1 × 2 rectangles (dominoes), or we may say, to cover the rectangle with dominoes. In how many distinct ways can this be done, where 2 solutions are distinct when they cannot be brought into coincidence by rotations and reflections?"

This author's solution to Patton's problem (published in the magazine's January, 1962, issue) goes as follows: First,

135

POLYOMINOES

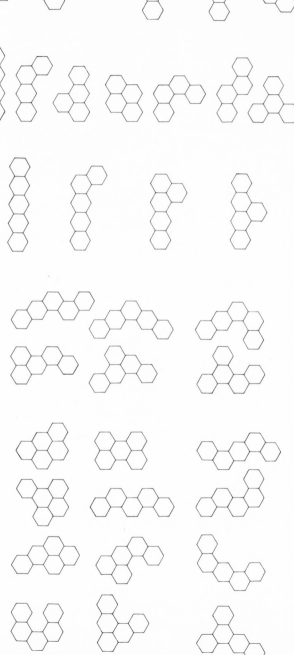

Figure 143. The hexagonal animals up through size 5.

136

all $2 \times n$ rectangles of dominoes are enumerated without regard to possible symmetries among them. For $n = 1$, the number of possible rectangles is $f_1 = 1$, and for $n = 2$, the 2 dominoes are either horizontal or vertical, so that $f_2 = 2$. For n greater than 2, starting at the left, the $2 \times n$ rectangle begins with either a vertical domino, which can be "extended" to fill out the $2 \times n$ rectangle in f_{n-1} ways, or with a pair of horizontal dominoes, which can be "extended" to fill out the rectangle in f_{n-2} ways. Hence $f_n = f_{n-1} + f_{n-2}$, as illustrated in Figure 144.

Figure 144. Filling a 2 × n rectangle with dominoes for n = 1, 2, 3, and 4.

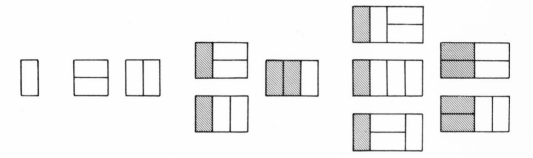

The sequence beginning $f_1 = 1$, $f_2 = 2$ and satisfying $f_n = f_{n-1} + f_{n-2}$ for n greater than 2 is the famous *Fibonacci sequence*: 1, 2, 3, 5, 8, 13, 21, 34, 55, 89, ... The thirteenth-century Italian mathematician Leonardo Fibonacci (also known as Leonardo of Pisa) first introduced this sequence to the mathematical world. He started with 0 and 1, then added these 2 terms together to get 1 again, and continued to generate each new term as the sum of its 2 immediate predecessors. Thus, in its original form, the sequence began: 0, 1, 1, 2, 3, 5, 8, 13, ...

Let C_m refer to the number of solutions to the $2 \times m$ rectangle in which left-to-right mirror images are *not* regarded as distinct. Then $C_m = \frac{1}{2}(f_m + s_m)$, where s_m is the number of solutions that are left-to-right symmetric. This result is a simple application of the formula $N = \frac{1}{2}(T + C)$ of Chapter V, used to count the number of distinct cases under an "involution." (As a direct derivation, the number that are not

137

left-to-right symmetric is clearly $f_m - s_m$, and only half of these asymmetric ones are distinct when left-to-right mirror images are considered to be the same. However, all the symmetric cases retain their individual identity, for a total of $\frac{1}{2}(f_m - s_m) + s_m = \frac{1}{2}(f_m + s_m)$.)

To evaluate s_m, consider odd and even m separately. For $m = 2n + 1$, a left-to-right symmetric solution must have a vertical domino in the center, leaving a $2 \times n$ rectangle on each side. One side can be completed in f_n ways, and then the other side is completely specified as the mirror image. Thus $s_{2n+1} = f_n$.

For $m = 2n$, a vertical line down the center of the rectangle either cuts a horizontal pair of dominoes or cuts no dominoes. In the former case there are f_{n-1} ways to specify the $2 \times (n - 1)$ rectangle to the left of the horizontal pair; in the latter case, f_n ways to specify the $2 \times n$ rectangle to the left of the midline; and, having specified the left half, one can determine the right half by mirror symmetry. Hence, $s_{2n} = f_{n-1} + f_n = f_{n+1}$.

Thus, $C_{2n+1} = \frac{1}{2}(f_{2n+1} + f_n)$ and $C_{2n} = \frac{1}{2}(f_{2n} + f_{n+1})$, which is the answer to the above problem except for the case $m = 2$, since the 2×2 rectangle is a square and admits of a 90-degree rotational symmetry, which reduces $C_2 = 2$ to $C'_2 = 1$, without affecting any other cases.

The following table summarizes the result.

n	Number of Covered $2 \times n$ Rectangles
1	1
2	1
3	$\frac{1}{2}(f_3 + f_1) = \frac{1}{2}(3 + 1) = 2$
4	$\frac{1}{2}(f_4 + f_3) = \frac{1}{2}(5 + 3) = 4$
5	$\frac{1}{2}(f_5 + f_2) = \frac{1}{2}(8 + 2) = 5$
6	$\frac{1}{2}(f_6 + f_4) = \frac{1}{2}(13 + 5) = 9$
7	$\frac{1}{2}(f_7 + f_3) = \frac{1}{2}(21 + 3) = 12$

n	Number of Covered $2 \times n$ Rectangles (*continued*)

8    $\frac{1}{2}(f_8 + f_5) = \frac{1}{2}(34 + 8) = 21$

9    $\frac{1}{2}(f_9 + f_4) = \frac{1}{2}(55 + 5) = 30$

10    $\frac{1}{2}(f_{10} + f_6) = \frac{1}{2}(89 + 13) = 51$

11    $\frac{1}{2}(f_{11} + f_5) = \frac{1}{2}(144 + 8) = 76$

12    $\frac{1}{2}(f_{12} + f_7) = \frac{1}{2}(233 + 21) = 127$

The number of coverings of the $3 \times n$ rectangle with dominoes is clearly a much more difficult problem, but the reader is invited to try. A much easier problem is to enumerate the number of ways to cover the $2 \times n$ rectangle, or even the $3 \times n$ rectangle, with right trominoes; the number of ways to cover the $4 \times n$ rectangle with right trominoes appears to be a challenging problem with reasonable hope of an attainable solution. The reader is encouraged to attempt it.

This ends our excursion into the fascinating realm of the polyomino. Inevitably, much that is interesting and exciting has been missed. The reader is invited to return to polyominoes frequently and to explore new paths on his own. The challenge of mathematical exploration is a never-ending source of enjoyment.

APPENDIX I

ANSWERS TO EXERCISES
IN CHAPTER V

Answers To Exercises in Chapter V

1. $8^2 \times 10^5 = 6{,}400{,}000.$

2. $12 \times 15 \times 9 \times 13 \times 11 \times 12 = 2{,}779{,}920.$

3. $26 \cdot 25 \cdot 24 - 1 = 15{,}599.$

4. $52 \cdot 51 \cdot 50 \cdot 49 \cdot 48 \cdot 47 = 14{,}658{,}134{,}400.$

5. $\binom{64}{4} = \dfrac{64 \cdot 63 \cdot 62 \cdot 61}{4 \cdot 3 \cdot 2 \cdot 1} = 635{,}376.$

6. $\binom{64}{8} = \dfrac{64 \cdot 63 \cdot 62 \cdot 61 \cdot 60 \cdot 59 \cdot 58 \cdot 57}{8 \cdot 7 \cdot 6 \cdot 5 \cdot 4 \cdot 3 \cdot 2 \cdot 1} = 4{,}426{,}165{,}368.$

7. $\binom{12}{6} = \dfrac{12 \cdot 11 \cdot 10 \cdot 9 \cdot 8 \cdot 7}{6 \cdot 5 \cdot 4 \cdot 3 \cdot 2 \cdot 1} = 924.$

8. $\binom{7}{3} = \dfrac{7 \cdot 6 \cdot 5}{3 \cdot 2 \cdot 1} = 35.$

9. $\binom{4 + 5 - 1}{5 - 1} = \binom{8}{4} = 70.$

1111	1112	4445	2235	1355
2222	1113	1555	2245	1455
3333	1114	2555	1233	2355
4444	1115	3555	1334	2455
5555	1222	4555	1335	3455
1122	2223	1123	2334	1234
1133	2224	1124	2335	1235
1144	2225	1125	3345	1245
1155	1333	1134	1244	1345
2233	2333	1135	1344	2345
2244	3334	1145	2344	
2255	3335	1223	1445	
3344	1444	1224	2445	
3355	2444	1225	3445	
4455	3444	2234	1255	

10. $\left(\begin{array}{c} 3 + 12 - 1 \\ 3 - 1 \end{array}\right) = \left(\begin{array}{c} 14 \\ 2 \end{array}\right) = 91.$

11. If there were extra marks on the symbols to make them all distinguishable, there would be $k!$ permutations. However, the k_1 symbols of the first type can be permuted among themselves in $k_1!$ ways, and the k_2 symbols of the second type can be independently permuted among themselves in $k_2!$ ways, and so on, leaving only $\dfrac{k!}{k_1!\, k_2! \cdots k_r!}$ distinguishable permutations.

12. For PEPPER, $\dfrac{6!}{3!\, 2!\, 1!} = 60$ permutations. For MISSISSIPPI,

$\dfrac{11!}{4!\, 4!\, 2!\, 1!} = 34{,}650$ permutations.

13.

n	No Factors in Common with n	$\phi(n)$
1	1	1
2	1	1
3	1, 2	2
4	1, 3	2
5	1, 2, 3, 4	4
6	1, 5	2
7	1, 2, 3, 4, 5, 6	6
8	1, 3, 5, 7	4
9	1, 2, 4, 5, 7, 8	6
10	1, 3, 7, 9	4
11	1, 2, 3, 4, 5, 6, 7, 8, 9, 10	10
12	1, 5, 7, 11	4
13	1, 2, 3, 4, 5, 6, 7, 8, 9, 10, 11, 12	12
14	1, 3, 5, 9, 11, 13	6
15	1, 2, 4, 7, 8, 11, 13, 14	8

14. The derivation of the formula is indicated in the "Hints." The rest is left to the reader.

15. The primes to 100 are: 2, 3, 5, 7, 11, 13, 17, 19, 23, 29, 31, 37, 41, 43, 47, 53, 59, 61, 67, 71, 73, 79, 83, 89, 97. By the formula,

$$\pi(100) = 4 - 1 + 100 - \left(\left[\frac{100}{2}\right] + \left[\frac{100}{3}\right] + \left[\frac{100}{5}\right] + \left[\frac{100}{7}\right]\right)$$

$$+ \left(\left[\frac{100}{6}\right] + \left[\frac{100}{10}\right] + \left[\frac{100}{14}\right] + \left[\frac{100}{15}\right] + \left[\frac{100}{21}\right] + \left[\frac{100}{35}\right]\right)$$

$$- \left(\left[\frac{100}{30}\right] + \left[\frac{100}{42}\right] + \left[\frac{100}{70}\right] + \left[\frac{100}{105}\right]\right) + \left[\frac{100}{210}\right]$$

$$= 103 - (50 + 33 + 20 + 14) + (16 + 10 + 7 + 6 + 4 + 2)$$

$$- (3 + 2 + 1 + 0) + 0 = 103 - 117 + 45 - 6 = 25.$$

16. Eighteen were healthy.

17. $\frac{1}{2}(T + C) = \frac{1}{2}(1000 + 100) = 550.$

18. $\frac{1}{2}(T + C) = \frac{1}{2}(26^4 + 26^2) = 228,826.$

19. When k is an even number, $N = \frac{1}{2}(n^k + n^{\frac{k}{2}}).$
    When k is an odd number, $N = \frac{1}{2}(n^k + n^{\frac{k+1}{2}}).$

20. Thirty-two.

21. Twenty-eight double-6 and 55 double-9 dominoes.

22. The 27 drawings will not be presented here.

23. $N = \frac{1}{4}[n^4 + 3n^2].$

24. $N = \frac{1}{4}(T + C_a + C_b + C_c) = \frac{1}{4}(5^6 + 5^3 + 5^3 + 5^4) = 4125.$

25. H, I, O, X.

26. With a and b both odd: $N = \frac{1}{4}(T + C_a + C_b + C_c) = \frac{1}{4}(2^{ab} + 2^{a\left(\frac{b+1}{2}\right)} + 2^{\left(\frac{a+1}{2}\right)b} + 2^{\frac{ab+1}{2}});$
    a and b both even: $N = \frac{1}{4}(T + C_a + C_b + C_c) = \frac{1}{4}(2^{ab} + 2^{\frac{ab}{2}} + 2^{\frac{ab}{2}} + 2^{\frac{ab}{2}}) = \frac{1}{4}(2^{ab} + 3 \cdot 2^{\frac{ab}{2}});$
    a odd, b even: $N = \frac{1}{4}(T + C_a + C_b + C_c) = \frac{1}{4}(2^{ab} + 2^{\frac{ab}{2}} + 2^{\left(\frac{a+1}{2}\right)b} + 2^{\frac{ab}{2}}).$

27. $N = \frac{1}{4}(3^4 + 2 \cdot 3 + 3^2) = 24.$

28. Twenty-four, as before. The rectangular pattern is:

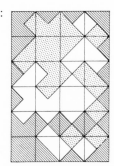

29. $N_4 = \frac{1}{4}(4^4 + 2 \cdot 4 + 4^2) = 70$.

$N_n = \frac{1}{4}(n^4 + 2n + n^2) = \frac{1}{4}n(n + 1)(n^2 - n + 2)$. If n or $n + 1$ is a multiple of 4, this is clearly an integer. However, in any case, one of n and $n + 1$ is even, and $n^2 - n + 2$ is always even, so that the product $n(n + 1)(n^2 - n + 2)$ is always a multiple of 4.

30. $N_2 = \frac{1}{4}(2^9 + 2 \cdot 2^3 + 2^5) = 140$.

31. $N_n = \frac{1}{4}(n^9 + 2 \cdot n^3 + n^5)$.

32. For even k, $N_n = \frac{1}{4}(n^{k^2} + 2 \cdot n^{\frac{1}{2}k^2} + n^{\frac{1}{2}k^2})$.

For odd k, $N_n = \frac{1}{4}(n^{k^2} + 2 \cdot n^{\frac{1}{4}(k^2+3)} + n^{\frac{1}{2}(k^2+1)})$.

33. An octomino symmetric under 90-degree rotation:

$$N_2 = \frac{1}{4}(2^8 + 2 \cdot 2^2 + 2^4) = 70.$$

34. $N = \frac{1}{4}(n^4 + 2 \cdot n + n^2)$.

35. $N = \frac{1}{8}(T + C_{180} + 2C_H + 2C_D) = \left[\frac{1}{8}\binom{9}{3} + 4 + 2 \cdot 10 + 2 \cdot 10\right] = 16$.

Three monominoes can be placed on a 3×3 board in the 16 following ways (each monomino is indicated by a dot):

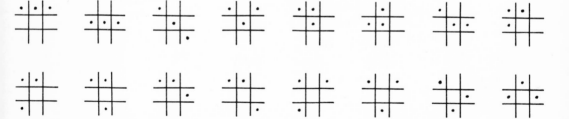

36. For the 4×4 board:

$$N_4 = \frac{1}{8}(T + C_{180} + 2C_{90} + 2C_H + 2C_D) = \frac{1}{8}\left\{\binom{16}{4} + \binom{8}{2} + 2 \cdot 4 + 2 \cdot \binom{8}{2} + 2 \cdot (1 + 6 \cdot 6 + 15)\right\} = 252.$$

For the 6 × 6 board:

$$N_6 = \tfrac{1}{8}\left\{\binom{36}{4} + \binom{18}{2} + 2\cdot 9 + 2\cdot\binom{18}{2} + 2\left[\binom{6}{4} + \binom{6}{2}\binom{15}{1} + \binom{15}{2}\right]\right\} = 7{,}509.$$

For the 8 × 8 board:

$$N_8 = \tfrac{1}{8}\left\{\binom{64}{4} + \binom{32}{2} + 2\cdot 16 + 2\cdot\binom{32}{2} + 2\left[\binom{8}{4} + \binom{8}{2}\binom{28}{1} + \binom{28}{2}\right]\right\} = 79{,}920.$$

37. $N = \tfrac{1}{8}(3^{16} + 3^8 + 2\cdot 3^4 + 2\cdot 3^8 + 2\cdot 3^{10}) = 5{,}398{,}083.$

38. $N = \tfrac{1}{8}\left[\binom{9}{5} + \binom{4}{2} + 2\cdot 2 + 2\cdot 12 + 2\cdot 12\right] = 23.$

39. $T = 3!\binom{8}{3}^2 = 18{,}816.$

$$N = \tfrac{1}{8}\left[18{,}816 + 0 + 2\cdot 0 + 2\cdot 0 + 2\cdot 4\cdot\binom{8}{3}\right] = 2{,}408.$$

40. For 1 monomino: $N_1 = \dfrac{n^2 + 2n}{8}$ for even n;

$N_1 = \dfrac{n^2 + 4n + 3}{8}$ for odd n.

For 2 monominoes: $N_2 = \tfrac{1}{16}(n^4 + 6n^2 - 4n)$ for even n; $N_2 = \tfrac{1}{16}(n^4 + 8n^2 - 8n - 1)$ for odd n.

41. The X pentomino has the symmetry group of the square. The I pentomino has that of the rectangle. The T, U, V, W, and Z pentominoes have involutional symmetry. The F, L, N, P, and Y pentominoes have only identity symmetries.

42. $N_3 = \tfrac{1}{8}(3^5 + 3^3 + 2\cdot 3^2 + 2\cdot 3^4 + 2\cdot 3^3) = 63$ altogether.
$N_{abc} = N_3 - 3N_2 + 3N_1 = 63 - 36 + 9 = 36$ ways that actually use all 3 colors.

43. Without regard for symmetries: $T_4 = 4\cdot 3\cdot 2\cdot 1 = 24$. For distinguishable cases under rotation and reflection:
$N_4 = \tfrac{1}{8}(24 + 8 + 2\cdot 2 + 0 + 2\cdot 10) = 7.$

44. For 6 rooks: $T_6 = 6! = 720.$

$$N_6 = \tfrac{1}{8}\left\{720 + 6\cdot 4\cdot 2 + 0 + 0 + 2\left[1 + \binom{6}{4} + \binom{6}{2}\cdot 3 + 15\right]\right\} = 115.$$

For 8 rooks: $T_8 = 8! = 40,320$.

$$N_8 = \tfrac{1}{8}\Big\{8! + (8\cdot6\cdot4\cdot2) + 2\cdot8 + 0 + 2\Big[1 + \binom{8}{6}\cdot1$$

$$+ \binom{8}{4}\cdot3\cdot1 + \binom{8}{2}\cdot5\cdot3\cdot1 + \binom{8}{0}\cdot7\cdot5\cdot3\cdot1\Big]\Big\} = 5,281.$$

45. $N = \tfrac{1}{6}(2^6 + 2 + 2^2 + 2^3 + 2^2 + 2) = 14$.

46. $N = \tfrac{1}{12}(2^6 + 2 + 2^2 + 2^3 + 2^2 + 2 + 3\cdot2^4 + 3\cdot2^3) = 13$.

47. With rotations only, and k colors, $N = \tfrac{1}{6}(k^6 + k^3 + 2k^2 + 2k)$. With rotations and reflections, and k colors, $N = \tfrac{1}{12}(k^6 + k^3 + 2k^2 + 2k + 3k^4 + 3k^3) = \tfrac{1}{12}(k^6 + 3k^4 + 4k^3 + 2k^2 + 2k)$. In particular, with rotations only, $N_3 = 130$ and $N_4 = 700$, while with rotations and reflections, $N_3 = 92$ and $N_4 = 430$.

48. $N = \tfrac{1}{6}(5^3 + 2\cdot5 + 3\cdot5^2) = 35$

49. The number of distinct strings is b^p. For the necklaces with the cyclic group of symmetries, $N = \dfrac{1}{p}[b^p + (p-1)b]$; with the dihedral group of symmetries, $N = \dfrac{1}{2p}[b^p + (p-1)b + pb^{\frac{p+1}{2}}]$.

For $b = 2$ and $p = 5$, both enumerations yield an answer of 8.

For $b = 4$ and $p = 3$, these numbers are 24 and 20, respectively.

50. The 24 symmetries are: 1 identity; 6 rotations by ±90 degrees about a face-to-face diagonal; 3 rotations by 180 degrees about a face-to-face diagonal; 6 rotations by 180 degrees about an edge-to-edge diagonal; 8 rotations by ±120 degrees about a vertex-to-vertex diagonal.

51. $N = \tfrac{1}{24}(6! + 0 + 0 + 0 + 0) = 30$.

52. $N = 2$.

53. $N = 6$.

54. When the number of labeled vertices is unrestricted,

$$N = \tfrac{1}{24}(2^8 + 6\cdot2^2 + 3\cdot2^4 + 6\cdot2^4 + 8\cdot2^4) = 23.$$

When there are 4 labeled and 4 unlabeled vertices,

$$N = \tfrac{1}{24}[\binom{8}{4} + 6\cdot2 + 3\cdot6 + 6\cdot6 + 8\cdot2^2] = 7.$$

APPENDIX II

PROBLEM COMPENDIUM

Problem Compendium

This compendium contains all the problems dealing with the fitting together of pentominoes and related polyominoes that are included in the book as well as a number of additional constructions.

PENTOMINO PROBLEMS

The patterns in Problems 1 through 32 can be covered exactly, using the 12 pentominoes. When an interesting special case is known (for example, construction from 2 identical pieces), it is indicated by a heavy line dividing the pattern.

1. Fit the 12 pentominoes into one 3 × 20 rectangle.
2. Again, using the 12 pentominoes, fit them into one 4 × 15 rectangle.
3. All 12 pentominoes can be fitted into one 5 × 12 rectangle.
4. Fit the pentominoes into one 6 × 10 rectangle.
5.

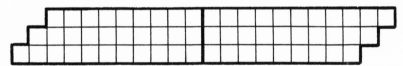

6.

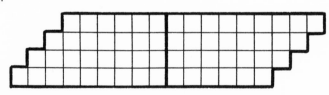

7.

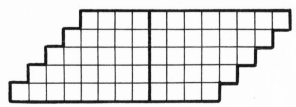

POLYOMINOES

8.

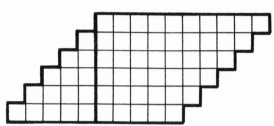

9.

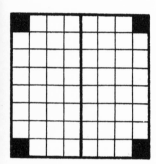

10.

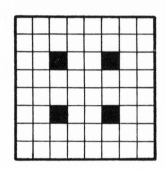

11.

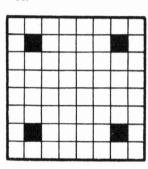

12.

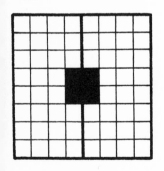

13.

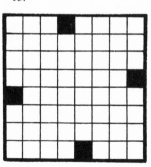

14.

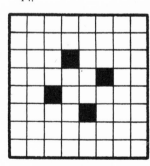

15.

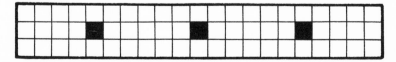

16.

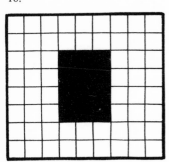

17.

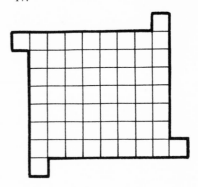

18.

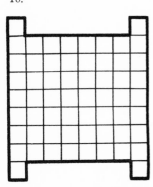

19.

20. Each of the 3 rectangles has 1 hole.

21. This 61-square pattern has a hole that, as was shown in Chapter IV, cannot be located in the center.

22. If the 8 × 8 square is constructed from the 2 congruent pieces as shown in the diagram on the left, the unshaded half may be shifted bodily to form the 9 × 7 rectangle shown on the right.

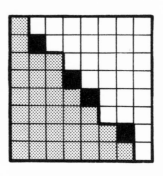
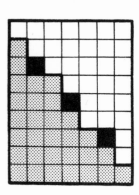

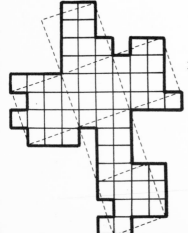

23. An unidentified reader of the *Fairy Chess Review* designed and solved this unusual problem. The 12 pentominoes will cover the irregular shape shown below, which can then be folded on the dashed lines to cover the surface of a cube as indicated.

24.

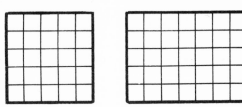

With 2,339 solutions to the basic 6 × 10 rectangular pattern, additional constraints may be imposed to make the problem more challenging. Some of the more interesting special cases of this pattern are given in Problems 25 through 32.

25. Construct two 6 × 5 rectangles.

26. The 6 × 10 rectangle contains a 3 × 5 subrectangle within it.

27. The 6 × 10 rectangle is constructed with a 4 × 5 subrectangle within it.

28. The 6 × 10 rectangle is constructed from the 2 pieces shown at the left. The unshaded half may be shifted as a unit to form the 9 × 7 rectangle shown at the right.

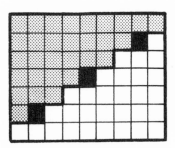

29. In a way similar to Problem 28, the unshaded portion of the 6 × 10 rectangle is shifted to form the 9 × 7 rectangle.

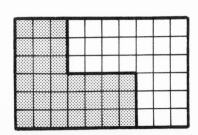
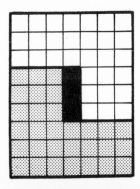

30. Build the 6 × 10 rectangle so that each of the 12 pentominoes touches an edge.

31. Build the 6 × 10 rectangle so that the I pentomino does not touch an edge.

32. Throw the 12 pentominoes randomly on the table. Now construct the 6 × 10 rectangle without turning over any of the pieces. (All 32 cases are possible.)

33. *The 10 Problem.* (a) Build a 10-square pattern with 2 of the pentominoes. Find 2 other pentominoes that will fill the same shape. (b) Use 4 of the remaining pieces to repeat the process. (c) Finally, use the last 4 pentominoes to repeat the process a third time. (The 10-square pattern of *b* need not be the same as the first, and the 10-square pattern of *c* may be different from both the first and second.)

34. *The 20 Problem.* Use 4 of the pentominoes to build a 20-square pattern. Use 4 others to build the *same* pattern again. The same pattern must now be constructed a third time with the last 4 pieces.

35. *The Double-Duplication Problem.* Use 2 pentominoes to build a 10-square pattern. Use 2 more pieces to repeat the shape. Use the remaining 8 pieces to build a model of the shape, but with each of the linear dimensions multiplied by 2. The figure below gives an example of one of the several shapes that can be constructed in this manner.

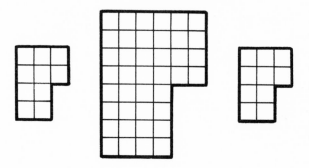

36. Figure 19 shows how the 12 pentominoes may be cut from a 6 × 13 rectangular piece of wood with a saw that does not cut around corners. Miss Alison Doig, of London, England, has re-

cently shown how this problem may be solved using either a 4 × 19 or a 5 × 15 piece of wood. The reader is invited to match Miss Doig's effort and to dissect the 5 × 15 rectangle below. (The U pentomino again requires special attention. Assume that it must be cut as a 2 × 3 rectangle and finished subsequently, by other means.)

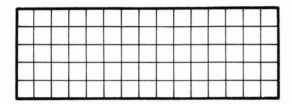

37. *The Triplication Problem.* Given a pentomino, use 9 of the other pentominoes to construct a scale model 3 times as wide and 3 times as high as the given piece. Construct all 12 pentomino triplications.

38. An even number of P pentominoes can easily cover a rectangle with an even area. Find the smallest rectangle that can be covered with an *odd* number of P pentominoes.

39. Make a 9 × 10 rectangle with the 18 one-sided pentominoes shown below. These pieces may not be turned over.

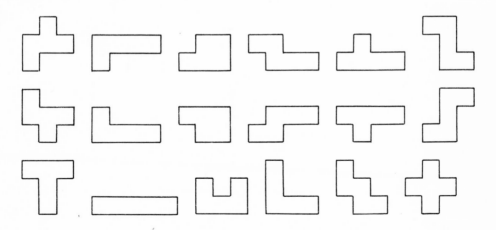

157

Problems 40 through 46 can be constructed using a set of solid pentominoes, that is, the 12 pentominoes, each constructed from 5 "unit cubes."

40. Construct a 3 × 4 × 5 solid.
41. Build a 2 × 5 × 6 solid. (This can be constructed from two 1 × 5 × 6 planar subunits.)
42. Build a 2 × 3 × 10 solid. (This cannot be constructed from two 1 × 3 × 10 subunits. However, a "minimum" solution, with only the L and Y pieces not wholly contained in one of the 1 × 3 × 10 planes, does exist.)
43. The Cinder Block (the shaded area is empty).

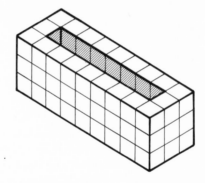

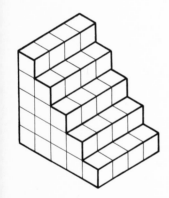

44. The Steps.

45. The Pyramid. Only 11 of the pieces are used for this shape, but it still ranks with the more difficult problems.

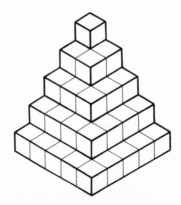

46. *Model Problems.* A solid model of a solid pentomino can be made with a volume of 60 cubes. The scale model is twice the length and twice the width of the solid pentomino, and is built 3 units deep. The figures below show the models of the T and U pentominoes constructed in such a fashion. The model of the U is particularly interesting since it can be inverted, as shown, and called a tunnel or arch. Of the 12 pentominoes, the I, L, P, N, T, U, V, Y, and Z are known to have solutions, the W and X are impossible, and whether or not the F has a solution is still undecided.

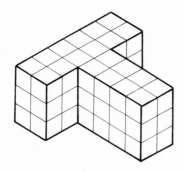 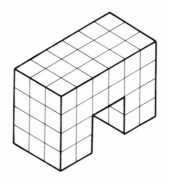

PENTACUBE PROBLEMS

Pentacubes, as noted earlier, use all solid pentominoes that are distinct under 3-dimensional rotation. A complete set consists of all possible combinations of 5 cubes connected on their faces. Problems 47 through 57 were all designed and solved by David A. Klarner. All the problems using 28 pieces can be solved with the "straight" pentacube omitted.

47. Construct a set of the 29 pentacubes and identify the 6 mirror-image pairs.

48. Use 28 of the pieces to construct a $2 \times 5 \times 14$ solid.

49. Use 28 of the pieces to construct a $2 \times 7 \times 10$ solid.

50. Use 28 of the pieces to construct a $4 \times 5 \times 7$ solid.

51. Find a simultaneous solution to the last 3 problems by constructing 2 solids, each $2 \times 5 \times 7$.

52. Construct the $2 \times 5 \times 14$ solid from 5 smaller rectangular solids.   159

53. Use 25 pieces to build a 5-unit cube. The 4 pieces omitted may be the 4 that have a linear dimension of 4 units or more.

54. Build a 7-layer pyramid. It is constructed like Problem 45 but with 2 more layers added to the bottom (a 6×6 and a 7×7 layer).

55. Use 27 of the pentacubes to build a model of a given pentacube. Build such models of all 29 pentacubes.

56. Use 28 of the pentacubes to build a cylinder 7 units high with its cross section of a model of one of the solid pentominoes. All 12 problems are possible.

57. *The Checkerboard.* Use 18 of the pentacubes to make a $3 \times 6 \times 6$ solid with alternate cubes missing from one of the 6×6 faces.

OTHER POLYOMINO PROBLEMS

Problems 58 through 61 use a combined set of the 12 pentominoes and the 5 tetrominoes.

58. Construct an 8×10 rectangle.

59. Using all the above pieces, build a 4×20 rectangle.

60. Obtain a simultaneous solution to the previous 2 problems by constructing two 4×10 rectangles.

61. Construct a 5×16 rectangle.

Problems 62–67. Use a set of the 35 hexominoes to build the patterns that follow. (These constructions first appeared in *Fairy Chess Review*.)

62.

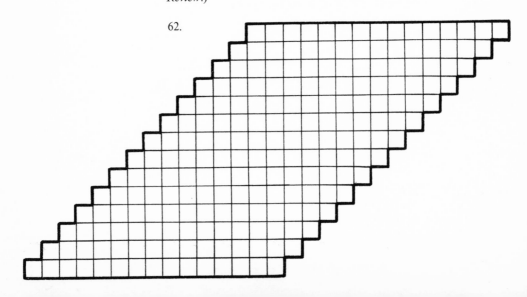

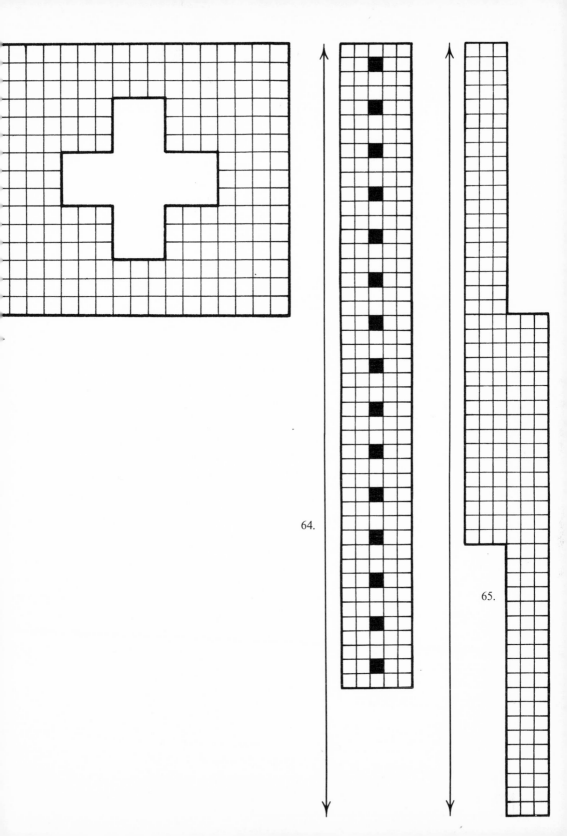

64.

65.

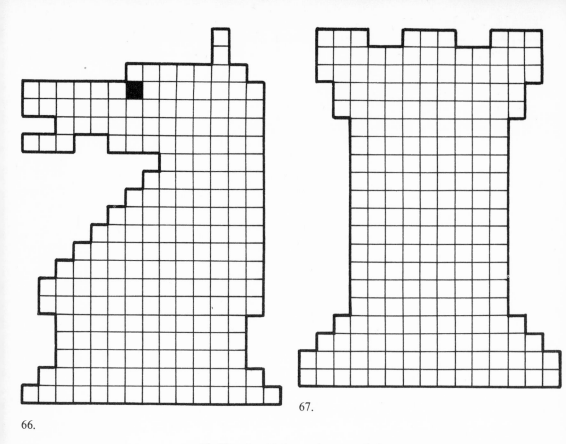

66.

67.

68. Use the 35 hexominoes and the 12 pentominoes to build an 18 × 15 rectangle. The special case indicated below has the pen-

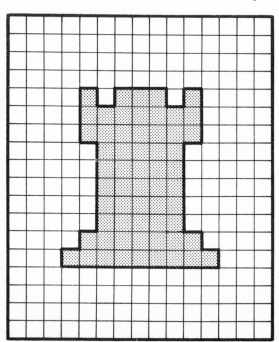

tominoes forming a "rook" in the center of the rectangle. (This problem also appeared in *Fairy Chess Review*.)

69. Use the 108 heptominoes to build three 11 × 23 rectangles each with a hole in the center (see Figure 103).

70. Discard the heptomino with the hole, and build a 107 × 7 rectangle with the remaining 107 heptominoes. This may be done by building four 7 × 25 rectangles and one 7 × 7 square (see Figure 104).

IMPOSSIBLE CONFIGURATIONS

The following problems all involve regions that the 12 pentominoes will not cover. For the asterisked problems, no simple impossibility proof has yet been discovered.

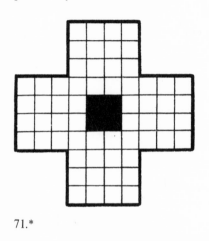

71.*

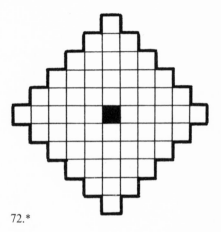

72.*

73.

POLYOMINOES

74.

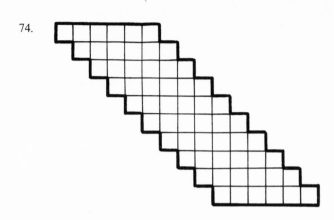

75.*

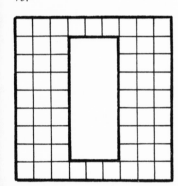

76.*

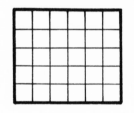

77.* Impossible with the 12 solid pentominoes.

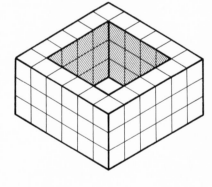

78. Impossible with the 12 solid pentominoes.

79.* The 3 × 20 rectangle constructed with the 12 pentominoes cannot be made from 2 smaller rectangles.

80. Place 4 monominoes on the 8 × 8 checkerboard without completely isolating any region of only a few squares, but in such a
   way that the 12 pentominoes will not cover the remainder of the
   board.

READERS' RESEARCH

The following pentomino problems are not known to have solutions, nor have they been proved impossible.

81.

82.

83.

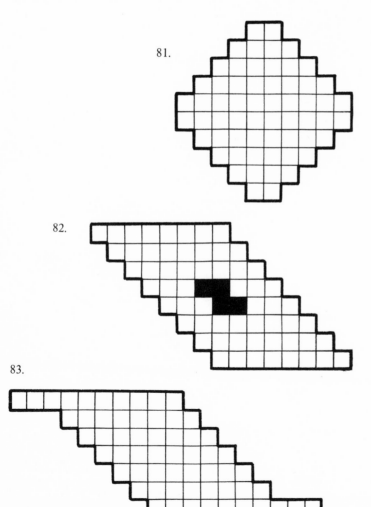

POLYOMINOES

Problems 24 and 25 are the only known solutions involving simultaneous rectangles (that is, 2 rectangles made out of the 12 pentominoes with no pentomino used more than once) and pentominoes. The only other results known on this topic are that simultaneous 3×10 and 6×5 rectangles cannot be constructed (Problem 76); the 3×20 rectangle cannot be constructed from 2 smaller rectangles (Problem 79); and a 2×10 and 4×10 rectangle cannot be constructed simultaneously. Problems 84 through 87 give other rectangular factorizations that might be possible.

84. Construct 4×5 and 5×8 simultaneous rectangles.

85. Build simultaneous 3×5 and 5×9 rectangles.

86. Simultaneous 4×5 and 4×10 rectangles are to be constructed.

87. Construct 2×10 and 5×8 simultaneous rectangles.

88. *The 15 Problem.* Can a pattern of 15 squares be found that can be constructed 4 times simultaneously from a set of the pentominoes? (*Cf.* Problems 33 and 34.)

89. Many variations on the 3×20 rectangle involve configurations with a 3-unit width. The cross below is typical of these possibilities.

90. Another variation of a 3 × 20 rectangle, with a hole in the center:

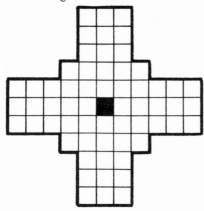

91. It is known that 9 of the pentominoes can be used to triplicate any given pentomino (see Problem 37). Can 9 sets be used to triplicate the complete set of 12 pentominoes?

92. Use the solid pentominoes to build the model of the F below.

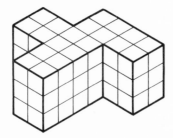

Undoubtedly the reader can invent many new polyomino and poly-cube problems for himself. There is also a great deal of unexplored problem territory based on the material in Chapter VII.

GLOSSARY

Glossary

B

Backtrack. A systematic search procedure for favorable configurations that uses trial and error to build up a configuration one element at a time.

Base. A number that is to be raised to a certain power, which is indicated by the superscript exponent.

Binomial Coefficients. The numbers $\binom{n}{k}$ that appear as coefficients in the binomial theorem and that also equal the number of ways to select a subset of k objects from a set of n objects.

Binomial Theorem. The algebraic formula:

$$(x + y)^n = x^n + \binom{n}{1}x^{n-1}y + \binom{n}{2}x^{n-2}y^2 + \cdots + \binom{n}{n-1}xy^{n-1} + \binom{n}{n}y^n.$$

Board. A rectangular array composed of equal-sized squares on which polyominoes may be fitted.

C

Checkerboard Coloring. The assignment of 2 colors to a board in such a way that adjacent squares are always of different colors.

Coefficient. A multiplier, or factor, in a mathematical term.

Combinatorial Analysis. The branch of mathematics dealing with geometric or numerical patterns, arrangements, permutations, combinations, and enumerations.

Combinatorial Geometry. The branch of combinatorial analysis concerned with geometric patterns.

Combination. An assortment of objects; for example, a social security number is a combination of decimal digits. An *ordered combination* is one in which the order of the objects is significant; a social security number is an ordered combination of 9 digits. In an *unordered combination,* the order in which the objects are arranged is not significant.

171

Cyclic Group. The symmetry group of a regular n-sided polygon consisting of the symmetry operators that rotate the figure through angles of 0 degrees, $\frac{1}{n} \cdot 360$, $\frac{2}{n} \cdot 360$, $\frac{3}{n} \cdot 360$, ... and $\frac{n-1}{n} \cdot 360$ degrees around its center (for a symmetry group of n symmetry operators).

D

Dekomino. A polyomino composed of 10 squares; there are 4466 different dekominoes.

Diamond. A triangular animal composed of 2 equilateral triangles.

Digit. A basic symbol used in the representation of numbers. In the decimal system, there are 10 different digit symbols: 0, 1, 2, 3, 4, 5, 6, 7, 8, and 9.

Dihedral Group. The symmetry group of a regular n-sided polygon containing all n rotation symmetries of the cyclic group in addition to the n reflection symmetries corresponding to reflecting the figure in any one of its n diagonals (the lines through the center of the figure terminating either in its vertices or in the midpoints of its sides).

Domino. A polyomino composed of 2 squares; it has only 1 shape.

E

Enumeration. Counting; the determination of the number of distinct cases, patterns, or arrangements in a set.

Exponent. A numerical superscript of a number indicating its power or the number of times the number should be multiplied by itself.

F

Factorial. With a whole number n, the product of all the integers from 1 to n inclusive. It equals the number of permutations on n distinct objects and is denoted by $n!$

G

Grid Line. A horizontal or vertical line across a board that does not intersect any square but runs between the edges of 2 adjoining squares.

Group. A set G of mathematical objects (such as numbers or symmetry operators), with a multiplication rule satisfying the following 4 requirements: (1) *Closure:* If a and b are objects in G, then $a \times b$ is a uniquely defined object in G. (2) *Associativity:* if a, b, and c are objects in G, then $a \times (b \times c) = (a \times b) \times c$. (3) *Identity element:* There is an object e in G such that $e \times a = a \times e = a$ for every a in G. This object e is called the identity element of G. (4) *Inverse element:* If a is an object in G, then there is an object a' in G such that $a \times a' = a' \times a = e$, where e is the identity element of G; a' is called the inverse of a.

Note: In general, group elements need not satisfy the *commutative law, $a \times b = b \times a$*. If this law is obeyed by all objects a and b of G, G is called a *commutative group.*

H

Heptiamond. A triangular animal composed of 7 equilateral triangles; there are 24 different heptiamonds.

Heptomino. A polyomino composed of 7 squares; there are 108 different heptominoes.

Hexagonal Animal. A pattern formed by a specific number of equal-sized regular hexagons connected by common edges.

Hexiamond. A triangular animal composed of 6 equilateral triangles; there are 12 different hexiamonds.

Hexomino. A polyomino composed of 6 squares; there are 35 different hexominoes.

I

Integer. A whole number. The positive integers are the numbers $1, 2, 3, 4, \ldots$; the negative integers are $-1, -2, -3, -4, \ldots$; and the remaining integer is 0.

M

Mathematical Induction. The name given to the deductive principle that: If $P(n)$ is a statement about the positive integers n, if it can be shown that $P(1)$ is true, and if it can be shown that the truth of $P(n + 1)$ follows from the truth of $P(n)$ for all positive integers n, then $P(n)$ is true in all cases.

Monomino. A single square; a polyomino of 1 square.

N

Nonomino. A polyomino composed of 9 squares; there are 1285 different nonominoes.

Number. A mathematical designator of quantity.

O

Octomino. A polyomino composed of 8 squares; there are 369 different octominoes.

Ordered Combination. See Combination.

P

Parity. The property of a number being either even or odd.

Parity Check. A test for the consistency of a mathematical statement based solely on the parity of the numbers involved.

Pentacube. A pattern composed of 5 equal-sized cubes connected by common faces; there are 29 different pentacubes.

Pentiamond. A triangular animal composed of 5 equilateral triangles. There are 4 different pentiamonds.

Pentomino. A polyomino composed of 5 squares; there are 12 possible pentominoes.

Permutation. A rearrangement or renumbering of the objects in a set.

Polyomino. A pattern formed by the connection of a specified number of equal-sized squares along common edges.

Polygon. A closed plane figure bounded by straight lines.

Pseudo-Polyomino. A pattern formed by several equal-sized squares connected either by common edges or joined at right angles by common vertices.

Q

Quasi-Polyomino. A pattern formed by several squares that need not even be connected but that can arise as a subset of the squares in a polyomino.

R

Reflection. Flipping over a geometric figure relative to a line or plane within it.

Rotation. Angular motion of a geometric figure relative to a point or line within it.

S

Set. Any collection of objects. Frequently, the objects in a set have some common characteristic; for example, all the dogs in China could be considered to be a set.

Solid Polyomino. A pattern formed by several equal-sized cubes connected by common faces; specifically, the figure resulting when the squares of a polyomino are replaced by cubes.

Subset. Part of a set, usually with some particular characteristic common to all its member objects. For example, the even numbers form a subset of the set of whole numbers.

Symmetry. A property of figures or configurations whereby the object looks the same after certain of its parts are interchanged.

Symmetry Group. A group composed of the symmetry operators of a particular geometric figure or mathematical configuration, where the "product" of 2 symmetry operators is that operator achieving in 1 step the same effect as that obtained by performing the 2 original symmetry operations one after the other. For example, the "product" of a 90-degree rotation and a 180-degree rotation is a 270-degree rotation.

Symmetry Operator. A systematic interchanging of parts of a figure in such a way that its appearance remains unchanged; for example, rotating a square 90 degrees round its center.

T

Tetromino. A polyomino composed of 4 squares; there are 5 different tetrominoes.

Triangular Animal. A pattern formed by several equal-sized equilateral triangles connected by common edges.

Tromino. A polyomino composed of 3 squares; there are 2 different trominoes.

U

Unordered Combination. See Combination.

W

Whole Number. See Integer.

BIBLIOGRAPHY

Bibliography

ARTICLES ON POLYOMINOES

Scientific American, "Mathematical Games Column" by Martin Gardner.

"About the Remarkable Similarity Between the Icosian Game and the Tower of Hanoi," CXCVI (May, 1957), 5, 154–156.

"More about Complex Dominoes, Plus the Answers to Last Month's Puzzles," CXCVII (December, 1957), 6, 126–129.

"A Game in Which Standard Pieces Composed of Cubes Are Assembled into Larger Forms" (Soma Cubes), CXCIX (September, 1958), 3, 182–188.

"More about the Shapes That Can Be Made with Complex Dominoes," CCIII (November, 1960), 5, 186–194.

"A New Collection of Brain Teasers," CCIV (June, 1961), 6, 168.

"Some Puzzles Based on Checkerboards and Answers to Last Month's Problems," CCVII (November, 1962), 5, 151–159.

Recreational Mathematics Magazine.

Solomon W. Golomb. "The General Theory of Polyominoes, Part 1, Dominoes, Pentominoes, and Checkerboards," No. 4 (August, 1961), 3–12.

———. "The General Theory of Polyominoes, Part 2, Patterns and Polyominoes," No. 5 (October, 1961), 3–12 (also *see* Notes, pp. 13–14).

———. "The General Theory of Polyominoes, Part 3, Pentomino Exclusion by Monominoes," No. 6 (December, 1961), 3–20.

———. "The General Theory of Polyominoes, Part 4, Extensions of Polyominoes," No. 8 (April, 1962), 7–16.

Anderson, Jean H. "Polyominoes—The 'Twenty Problem,' " No. 9 (June, 1962), 25–30.

"Polyominoes—The 'Twenty Problem' and Others," No. 10 (August, 1962), 25–28.

New Scientist, "Puzzles and Paradoxes" column by T. H. O'Beirne.

"Pell's Equation in Two Popular Problems," No. 258 (October 26, 1961), 260–261.

"Pentominoes and Hexiamonds," No. 259 (November 2, 1961), 316–317.

"Some Hexiamond Solutions and an Introduction to a Set of 25 Remarkable Points," No. 260 (November 9, 1961), 379–380.

"For Boys, Men and Heroes," No. 266 (December 21, 1961), 751–752.

"Some Tetrabolical Difficulties," No. 270 (January 18, 1962), 158–159.

Fairy Chess Review.

Dawson, T. R., and W. E. Lester. "A Notation for Dissection Problems," III (April, 1937), 5, 46–47.

Stead, W. "Dissection," IX (December, 1954), 1, 2–4.

Various Mathematics Journals.

Golomb, Solomon, W. "Checkerboards and Polyominoes," *American Mathematical Monthly,* LXI (December, 1954), 10, 672–682.

Reeve, J. E., and J. A. Tyrrell. "Maestro Puzzles," *Mathematical Gazette,* XLV (1961), 97–99.

Read, R. C., "Contributions to the Cell Growth Problem," *Canadian Journal of Mathematics,* XIV (1962), 1, 1–20.

Hajtman, Bela, "On Coverings of Generalized Checkerboards I," *Magyar Tud. Akad. Mat. Kutato Int. Köze.,* VII (1962), 53–71.

*BOOKS CONTAINING
POLYOMINO MATERIAL*

Dudeney, H. E., *The Canterbury Puzzles.* New York: Dover Publications, Inc., 1958. Problem 74, "The Broken Chessboard," pp. 119–120.

Gardner, Martin. *The Scientific American Book of Mathematical Puzzles and Diversions.* New York: Simon and Schuster, 1959. Pp. 124–140.

———. *The Second Scientific American Book of Mathematical Puzzles and Diversions.* New York: Simon and Schuster, 1961. Chapter Six, "The Soma Cube," pp. 65–77.

Hunter, J. A., and Joseph S. Madachy. *Mathematical Diversions.* New York: D. Van Nostrand Company, Inc., 1963. Chapter Eight, "Fun with Shapes," pp. 77–89.

MORE TECHNICAL COMBINATORIAL
MATERIAL IN ARTICLES AND BOOKS

Scott, Dana S. "Programming a Combinatorial Puzzle." Unpublished study. Department of Electrical Engineering, Princeton University, Princeton, N. J., June 10, 1958.

Riordan, John. *An Introduction to Combinatorial Analysis.* New York: John Wiley, Inc., 1958.

Golomb, Solomon W. "A Mathematical Theory of Discrete Classification." *Fourth London Symposium on Information Theory.* London: Butterworth, 1961. Pp. 404–425.

181

ABOUT THE AUTHOR

SOLOMON W. GOLOMB was a graduate student at Harvard University when he introduced polyominoes to American puzzle fans during a talk before the Harvard Mathematics Club. While studying for the Ph.D., Dr. Golomb spent a year in Norway as a Fulbright Scholar.

He returned to the United States in 1956 and joined the Jet Propulsion Laboratory of the California Institute of Technology, where he directed research in space communications and now serves as a consultant. He is currently Professor of Electrical Engineering and Mathematics at the University of Southern California, where he applies his skills in combinatorial analysis to problems of coding and communications in such fields as information theory, genetics, computers, and statistics.

Dr. Golomb has written a number of articles on polyominoes and delivered innumerable lectures on the subject. His principal hobbies after polyominoes are games and puzzles of all sorts and learning new languages.

182

AP

A

l